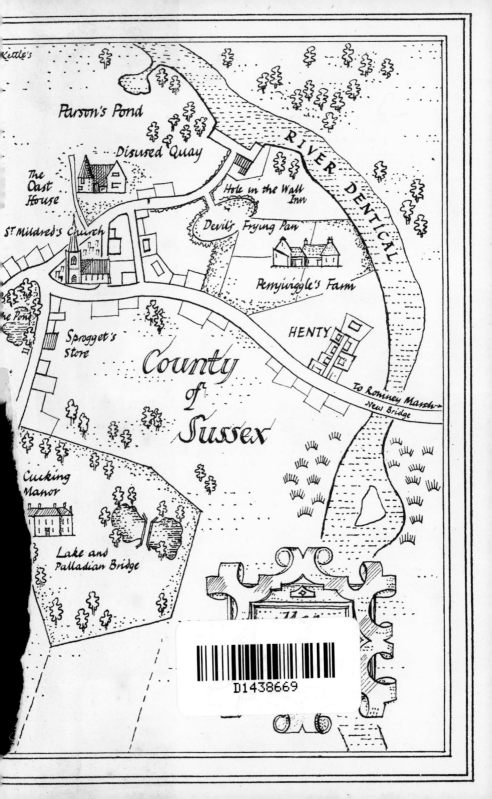

Kettle's

Parson's Pond

Disused Quay

The
Oast
House

St Mildred's Church

Hole in the Wall
Inn

Devil's Frying Pan

RIVER DENTICAL

Pennywiggle's Farm

HENTY

To Romney Marsh
New Bridge

ne Pond

Sprogget's
Store

County
of
Sussex

Cucking
Manor

Lake and
Palladian Bridge

D1438669

THE WICKED VILLAGE

By Donald McCormick

DONALD McCORMICK

The Wicked Village

Decorations by

J. MARCHBANK SALMON

JARROLDS

JARROLDS PUBLISHERS (*London*) LTD
178–202 Great Portland Street, London, W.1

AN IMPRINT OF THE   HUTCHINSON GROUP

London Melbourne Sydney
Auckland Bombay Toronto
Johannesburg New York

First published 1960

*This book has been set in Fournier type
face. It has been printed in Great Britain on
Antique Wove paper by Taylor Garnett
Evans & Co. Ltd., Watford, Herts, and
bound by them*

Contents

Preface

IT is just possible that some people, having read this book, might wish to visit 'The Wicked Village'. Therefore I am writing this preface to save them from poring over gazetteers and atlases with misguided zeal.

Codiham, I must sadly confess, doesn't exist.

Yet, having made this admission, I must add that everything about Codiham has its basis in fact. Had I written about a real village and its living inhabitants, the laws of libel and a sense of fair play would inevitably have inhibited me. There would then have been the reality without the substance, a portrait of rural rectitude without the sugar and spice of gossip and scandal.

Codiham is a composite creation of many features and distinctive landmarks of several villages in Sussex. All its buildings, institutions, inns, green, pond, river and church are based on places, organizations and customs which do exist. Occasionally I have borrowed material from other counties, but only when such components would not be out of place in that part of East Sussex in which Codiham is set. Saint Mildred's is remarkably like a church of the same name in a neighbouring county and the travelling teenage bell-ringers of Codiham share the enthusiasms of the Society of Rambling Ringers in Yorkshire.

The inhabitants of the village are entirely imaginary with three exceptions. The sole living trio in this story comprises my wife, my son and myself. The converted oast house in which we actually live is identical with that described in these pages, except that it has been transported to Codiham, and every chapter has been written in my 'ivory tower' under the swinging cowl of the oast.

I hope you will feel that Codiham is real, even it it doesn't exist, an abstract paradox which isn't as absurd as it sounds. For, though they become fewer every year, such off-beat and off-the-beaten-track villages may still be found and, if you take the trouble, you may appreciate the characteristics of Codiham in a score of different places. Indeed it is possible to make an amusing game out of trying to identify the origins of *The Wicked Village's* substance.

To encourage you to use *The Wicked Village* as a guide book, I shall try very briefly to pass on a few clues. Disregard any cynical townsman who will tell you that some of the things described herein couldn't happen today. If you venture as far afield as a tiny hamlet called Ebernoe in West Sussex, you will find villagers who still brew their own beer and cider and, with recipes handed down by their forefathers, make elderberry and parsnip wine and roast a sheep on the village green at the annual Horn Fair.

If you want to sample a home-made cherry brandy as good as that at the Merry Damsel in Codiham, call in at the Cherry Brandy House at Sarre in the Isle of Thanet. You will find characters as amusing and colourful as 'Sailor' Thompsett in the 'Creeks' around Bosham and at Rye Harbour.

But you must use your own initiative in this game. I will merely add that there are also many villages which are secretly proud of a reputation for 'wickedness' and an old gravestone in Selsey Churchyard once recorded the legend:

> Here lies ———'s daughter, Charlotte,
> Who was born a virgin and died a harlot.
> For fifteen years she kept her virginity,
> Not a bad record for this vicinity.

And if you delve into the history of Brede in East Sussex, you can hardly fail to recognize the origin of the story of Codiham's cannibalistic squire.

I even know a village green where a strange amorous rite uncannily like 'cucking' is still practised. But that would be telling! You must find out for yourselves.

1. It all started with beds

THOSE who make a habit of thinking in slick, staccato generalizations say that to write a successful book today is is necessary to introduce either a body (preferably already in a state of *rigor mortis*), or a bed into the first paragraph.

Of course there are writers with sufficient talent both for material success and macabre detail to solve the problem by producing a dead body in a bed in the vital first sentence. One genius has even gone one better and managed to enjoy the best of both schools of thought by supplying the body dead, the bed seductive and the body beautiful all neatly tucked up together in the same paragraph.

This reference to beds, if not bodies, is not as irrelevant as it may at first appear. For it is neither slick, nor a generalization to say that this book owes its origin to a certain bed – as seductive a bed as one is ever likely to come across – as the solitary clue to the solution of a pressing domestic problem.

Which may all sound about as mysterious as one of those silly television guessing games. Yet, really it is all quite simple in the sense that an obscurely silly association of ideas often provides the sole missing link in some unwieldy chain of a problem. For the simple, silly things of life have a fashion of opening up new horizons.

It all began with an idea I had. A bad idea. I ought to have known

9

better, but in my ignorance, inspired by the soliloquy with which I have opened this chapter, I decided it would be a good plan to write a book about beds. After all, I argued, there must be plenty to write about: Queen Elizabeth I alone must have slept in enough to provide at least one chapter. There was the Great Bed of Ware: what was it that Shakespeare had said? 'As many lies as will lie in a sheet of paper, although the sheet were big enough for the Bed of Ware.' And, come to think of it, Ben Jonson had written about this monolithic piece of furniture in *The Silent Woman*; Byron had referred to it in *Don Juan*, while Dickens also had something to offer on the subject.

There were truckle beds and trundle beds, hammocks in which matelots' floozies showed a leg when the master-at-arms came round . . . bundling beds in Wales, sleeping-bags and beds of nails. One couldn't go wrong.

In triumphant mood I set off for the British Museum to seek more information on beds. And while it is relatively easy, by consulting the black-bound alphabetical indices, to find out all about Bishop Bedell, Thomas Lovell Beddoes or Bedivere, the quest for the commonplace, or uncommonplace bed is much more complex. I mused here and browsed there, a lame researcher trying to negotiate the stiles of baffling indices, cross references, pressmarks, Rymer, *Foedera Circ. 22b.*, and the problem of finding the North library without losing oneself in the ladies' cloakroom.

I need not have troubled. I was swiftly disillusioned as it became apparent that far too many people, both ancient and modern, had already written books about beds.

Returning home, it was no consolation to be confronted by my wife who, with the happy complacency of one who is shortly to be praised for having made A Great Discovery, handed me a cutting from a magazine article on 'Inns Worth Visiting'. It read:

'Less well known is the MERRY DAMSEL at Codiham. Mainly interesting because it contains the celebrated King's Damsel's Bed mentioned in the diaries of Mrs. Aphra Behn, a finely carved Restoration period circular bed, twelve feet in diameter, ornamented with gilded cupids and maidens on the exquisitely wrought bronze posts. Charles II slept here, which explains the title given to the bed.'

'Sounds worth inspecting. Pleased, darling?' asked Sylvia obviously terribly bucked herself.

I felt like tearing the cutting into tiny pieces and dropping them in the fire. But the bright, eager, thought-this-would-help-you-my-sweet look in her eyes moved me to the compassion which is born of disappointment.

'Oh, jolly good,' I replied. 'How clever of you to spot it.'

I put the clipping in my pocket and thought no more about it. When asked how the 'book about beds' was getting on, I grunted non-committally. An author rarely admits to his nearest and dearest the awful truth when he hasn't an idea in his head. And at that time I was wallowing in a kind of Nirvana where ideas refuse to penetrate.

'You are beginning to get as stale as an old piece of Camembert,' my wife sagely observed one night.

And then I knew she had vaguely guessed I had nothing to write about.

'Perhaps we all are,' I hazarded defensively.

'And I'll tell you what the answer is,' she went on, warming to her theme. 'We have got into a rut. We need to make a move.'

'In other words,' I added, irritably, 'you think we should indulge in the good old parlour game of escapism, conjuring up all the most improbable places we might settle in.'

'Darling, I'm serious for once. We really *are* getting stale and frittering away our lives. I don't suggest anything wildly impossible such as going to Tahiti or Ibiza, or grubbing along in one of those dirty little Portuguese villages. Or even to buy an island, and play at being pioneers, neither of us being fitted for such a role.

'After all, we have done quite a bit of lotus-eating in our time. It was fun living in a *kasbah* for three years, but romance is apt to be rather unhygienic and insecure. Not that I am wildly devoted to security, but I do want some place that fits our faces and where we can make a real life. How can one be other than stale living in a flat in Ealing? What do we do with ourselves here? No garden to sit in, just a dull row of horrid, solid Victorian three-storey buildings to look out on. And not even any friends to ask in!'

'Oh, come now,' I remonstrated. 'It isn't as bad as that. There are the A——s and the W——s.'

'They aren't friends, only acquaintances. Now aren't they?'

'Now you mention it, I suppose they are. But what about F——? And S——?'

'F—— we only see about once a year and, as for S——, what possible use is *she* in an emergency?'

'Well, I see your point. I hadn't looked at it like that before. But what do you suggest?'

'That we start looking for a real home where we can make some sort of a life.'

'But that's exasperatingly vague, my sweet. What do you really want?'

'The awful thing is I don't honestly know for certain. I just have a hunch I should recognize the right place when I see it, if we look hard enough. And that's how I'd like it to happen – just to wander off into the country, turn a corner and be able to say, "Stop! That's it".'

.   .   .   .   .

It was from such vague gropings after the truth, such incoherency that eventually we came to the conclusion we had better start home-hunting. It was as though, quite suddenly, an awful revelation had been made to us. Until recently life had seemed, if not luxurious or wildly exciting, at least pleasantly eventful in London. Now it appeared like an eternal journey on an underground railway escalator with stolid rows of unseeing, unfeeling faces either side of us. Lots of people, but no real friends. Escapism is the illegitimate child of Mental Staleness out of Daily Routine.

We both of us had a horror of the phrase 'house-hunting'; we knew from past experience how searing, soul-destroying and mentally unbalancing it can become. In the end, after months of weary questing, it usually resulted in buying something one didn't want out of sheer desperation. So we made a pact that, come what may, neither of us should use that dreadful phrase, and that, because we set out to find somewhere to live, we should approach the whole task flippantly and treat it as a game.

On reflection I seriously recommend this approach to any couple or family about to embark on house-hunting. First of all, ban the phrase from your vocabulary; secondly, turn the whole affair into a winter evening's game. Switch off the television, hand round papers and pencils to all members of the family and see whether you can build up a composite picture of the sort of home and homeship you want. This may not find you the home, but it will go a surprisingly long way towards solving your problem. It may convince you that your ideas are all so diverse that you had better stay where you are. If, by argument and persuasion, you can agree upon the Dream Picture, then you will at least know exactly what you do want, and, even more important, what you *don't* want.

We played this game at mealtimes, we played it long after midnight in bed, with the eiderdowns littered with maps and guide-books; we played it individually while day-dreaming on trains and buses and collectively with pencil and paper round the fireside. I compiled a long list of questions which each of us had to answer; the results told us far more about each other than we had ever guessed before.

The answers to the first question were, fortunately, unanimous, otherwise we might still be in Ealing. We all decided that the sort of place we wished to live in was neither a city, a suburb, nor a town, but a village. Having decided this much, we called our game Villagemanship. The remaining questions were designed to produce the family's version of the Perfect Village. We defined Villagemanship rather pompously as the art of enabling townspeople to live a full life in the country. It really was a very silly definition which would thoroughly merit the guffaws with which it would have been greeted by the customers in a rustic tap-room.

'What we do *not* want,' chipped in Sylvia with feminine realism, 'is the sort of village which is really a dormitory for tired Londoners.'

Here she hit upon a great truth for suburbia today exists in the most frightening guise of all in many lovely villages where film stars, models and stockbrokers consider it's the thing to do to have a week-end hide-out. This has vitiated Villagemanship (as practised by the philistines) into a quest for cheap, dilapidated cottages, stinking of dry rot and wood worm. It may be a converted piggery, or a barn in a Maria Marten setting, with a king-post, but no sanitation. It isn't civilized, but it provides just the right excuse for *ye olde worlde snobbe* and an admirable opportunity for bringing off a non-taxable capital gain within a few years. By which time the stockbroker, model or film star will have sought out another village in which to perform the same disturbing antics.

Because of the invasion of the countryside by week-end cottagers we deleted much of the Thames Valley from our list of 'places to be seen'. Meanwhile, in preparation for our tour of villages, we read as many books about the countryside as we could find. But, while we found in them much that was enthralling and exciting in print, we were also sent on many false journeys. I recall being entranced by that ancient couplet:

> Oh, rare Northiam, thou dost far exceed
> Beckley, Peasmarsh, Udimore and Brede.

Alas, when we visited Northiam we did not think it rivalled, let alone exceeded the charms of the other places. Guide-books painted a picture of a glorious village green on which was a 'grand old oak' underneath which Queen Elizabeth I once had lunch and changed her shoes. The green consisted of two narrow patches of bumpy land and overgrown grass; as for the tree, it was a poor, gnarled wreck of an oak held together by rusty chains. Yet even so fastidious and careful an essayist as E. V. Lucas wrote of Northiam as being 'a village apart'.

So many of the villages that might have been suitable fifty years ago were today clumsy, sprawling, unlovely urban districts. Crawley and Bracknell had become 'new towns'; hamlets of Hertfordshire were marred by that form of modern building which can be likened to architectural elephantiasis.

On the other hand we didn't want anything arty-crafty, Francesca da Rimini, jimminy-quiminy, or the kind of folk-dancing, loom-weaving, blue-stocking's paradise which Ruskin and William Morris might have conjured up between them. Pottery and prudery, maypoles and majolica. Ours was no exercise in aestheticism; nor did we seek a much-vaunted, over-publicized, picture postcard village with tea-rooms in Tudor cottages every few yards. We agreed that Mr. Francis Brett Young's Monk's Norton and Mr. Beverley Nichols's Allways were delightful in woodcuts, but not really quite the model for a family bursting to do something more than bottle raspberries, listen to Mr. Follows's sermons and spend one's life going up and down the garden path. For the record – and it is absolutely essential that this should be made clear from the outset – we were not gardeners. We knew nothing of the alleged pleasures and more obvious agonies of this particular pursuit; we abhorred the idea of spending our leisure moments mowing the lawn, digging up potatoes, or pruning rose bushes.

But do not think we were agreed upon everything. My son had a passion for a smugglers' village, with an inn with secret passages under the stairs and a manor house with a lady ghost who walked at midnight with her lover's head under her arm. All else he stipulated was that there should be a village green on which cricket could be played.

My wife had a yen for 'something spacious and elegant. Whatever it is, it mustn't be claustrophobic with narrow streets and an air of genteel decay.' Which, as one might expect, ruled out quite a number of otherwise promising places. And, she added, it must be more than a hamlet: 'I don't want to do my shopping permanently at a one-eyed village store.'

My own preferences were for somewhere remote and off the gaunt, white arteries of teeming traffic, away from the stink of petrol and the sound of any form of engine except a motor lawn-motor. I have a deep and ineradicable hatred of motor-cars and motorists and would welcome any move to ration their petrol. But Sylvia shuddered at my suggestions. She had visions of our living in a Cold Comfort Farm atmosphere with leering Seths and a host of hostile Starkadders as neighbours. 'They'll simply ooze their contempt for us and delight in pointing out that we must walk two miles to the nearest shop,' she warned. 'Think of having a "daily" who talked scattily of having seen something nasty in the wood-shed, or being snowed up at Christmas and all the burst-pipe problems.' It was in vain that I pointed out that burst pipes were just as likely in a London suburb as in the remotest parts of the countryside.

I also insisted that the village should have at least three good pubs – enough to provide a reasonable 'crawl' and all within walking distance.

We couldn't agree about which was the pleasantest county in which to live. We should have liked Suffolk, or Wiltshire, but decided they were too inaccessible and that, if we were to explore far afield, all our savings for the new home would be spent long before we found it. But we rather hedged on this resolution when one evening we tried a variation of Villagemanship. The idea was a romantic fantasy: to scan all the guide-books and gazetteers for names that would be so attractive we should be incapable of avoiding their allurement. This led us as far astray as Dorset, where are to be found some of the most mellifluous village names in the English language. There is that line of John Betjeman's:

> Lord's Day bells from Bingham's Melcombe,
>   Iwerne Minster, Shroton, Plush,
> Down the grass between the beeches, mellow
>   in the evening hush.

Yes, there is Plush in Dorset not far from Ryme Intrinsica. It is so lovely that, if we had had the money, I think we should have bought it. For here was a whole village for sale – just a row of thatched cottages, with a manor house and pub about to go under the auctioneer's hammer.

But we certainly hadn't the capital to set up as lord and lady of the manor, nor any such archaic pretensions. And in any case Plush was a hamlet . . . need I say more?

We spent many nights scanning maps for improbable names. It is amazing what strange names you come across in the English countryside, if you take the trouble to look. . . . Warmley, Idle and Inwardleigh,

Foxholes-with-Boythorpe, Love Green, Lovelands and Lovely Seat; Blubberhouses, Wrangle, Sinwell and Ugley, the last-named being one of the prettiest villages in Essex. The lovely and the unlovely are incongruously mixed up so that often the loveliest names flatter to deceive and those which sound awful hide the identity of exquisite townships. Of course, this game becomes so fascinating the longer you play it that soon you lose sight of the real purpose of the exercise. At Christmas we had a competition for the best really ugly name: the winners were Shallow Bowels, Sewers End (Essex) and Black Dunghill in Devonshire! For sheer zaniness I awarded the prize to Christmas Pie (Surrey), Boozer's Pit (Cornwall), Stratton Strawless (I forget where this was) and Drinker's End (Gloucestershire).

And so we quested on, foolishly, haphazardly, occasionally methodically, but mostly merely hopefully. A great deal of time was wasted in playing at Villagemanship and little spent in actually viewing houses. As I have said, that part of the programme was one which we shied from most, for once you get to the stage of positively looking at houses, romance disappears and hard-headed bargaining begins. And it was the world of hard-headed bargaining from which we wished to escape. We were quite prepared to admit that there was 'room at the top', but also recognized that the summit, whether viewed politically, or personally, is a pretty bloody place. It is always possible to reach the top, if only for a day, but it is a mighty uncomfortable place, an undesirable residence, in fact. Our view was that in the long run there is probably much more fun at the bottom. This urge should not be regarded as either naïve or crude coherency, but simply a family's way of wanting to escape from the monotony of keeping up with the Joneses. A cock of the snook at suburbia, subtopia, The Never-Never-Had-It-So-Good-Land of subluminal electioneering, bossdom, the metropolis, insane ambition and the phoney-brassière world of assessing values by the size of one's house, car, fridge, the dimensions of a television screen, or the quantity of L.P. records.

Eventually we narrowed our potential searching round down to the south-eastern fringes of Surrey, the whole of Sussex and Kent south of a line drawn from just below Haslemere, through East Grinstead and Headcorn to Folkestone. This gave us the advantage of a vast area of Downland scheduled by the National Parks Commission and the lonely acres of Romney Marsh. Yet even in this area there were several suburbanized territories which had to be ignored. Many villages whose names looked splendid when embossed on writing-paper turned out to be disappointingly prosaic. And in a vague, rather angry, get-away-from-it-all mood, we still wanted romance in our dream village. Not the spurious romance of Edwardian village historians, nor the commercialized romance of *ye olde spinning wheele*, but romance in its most robust form – the colourful, gay life of a free, happy and attractive people.

But what people? And where to find them? We had our doubts. Kent was one of the loveliest of counties, yet the majority of its inhabitants spoke a horrible, mangled jargon that was neither country, nor cockney, but a toneless dirge of colourless short sentences that might easily be the lingo of the dimmer suburbs. It is a gross travesty of speech which threatens to absorb all the various county accents of the South of England and reduce them to a standardized flatness of speech and perpetual whine which could well be the moronic swan song of the Hellfare State.

We wished to avoid these dreary accents just as much as we wanted to escape from the equally flat, insincere artificiality of the unaristocratic lingo of the new demi-educated suburban bossman and his memsahib. Not that we wished to live in an Eden Philpotts stage setting, surrounded by Uncle Tom Cobley and all. But I have always felt that so much that is beautiful in southern England is marred by the monosyllabic whine of its inhabitants. 'If only,' I said to Sylvia, 'one could re-populate an English village with Welshmen and Irish women, how splendid it could be.'

'The result,' she promptly replied, 'would be a revolting parody of *Under Milk Wood.*'

She was probably right. One can't have everything.

· · · · ·

So the months passed by in a procession of villages visited and revisited, courted, jilted, doted on and finally sadly rejected. Horam, Piddinghoe, Tenterden, Goudhurst, Petworth, Sutton Valence, Ninfield, Lindfield, Billingshurst, Hawkhurst and Benenden. All had something, all lacked something. We inspected them and spurned them, loved them all in their way and then went on ours.

They all lacked – what shall I say? – a touch of devilment. We wanted in our muddy, subconscious reaches, a touch of the *matoufan*, of which de Maupassant wrote, a hint of Puckishness, of Elizabethan swagger and that element of scallywaggery which Lin Yutang praises as one of the keys that open the door to life. The Wicked City, the Wicked City . . .

we couldn't forget our *kasbah* past, the halcyon years of our prolonged honeymoon in Algeria. Wickedness was there, but it didn't depress one. It was the wickedness which entertained, which deserved redemption and, Allah be praised, which increased one's respect for human life.

I cannot explain this. I do not pretend to explain it. But wickedness, not in its puritanical sense, but rather in the spirit of the classical humanists, drew us as kindred spirits. In the midst of wickedness we should feel at home.

Obviously as a family we must have long since become in the eyes of a coldly clinical world what bureaucracy would call a psychiatric case-history. We worked, we played, albeit a trifle sadly, in London; we day-dreamed with inhibitions and reservations; we were in the main law-abiding and not especially devoted to eccentricities of conduct. And yet, though not anti-social, we yearned for an element of wickedness.

One summer's evening, when the *matoufan* spirit was on me strongly, I went alone to see a converted stables at Fordcombe, some few miles from Tunbridge Wells. It was one of those forlorn quarter chances which did not merit a visit by the entire family. Alone, hot and thirsty, like a roaming rogue elephant, hell-bent on I knew not what, I stumped angrily over the ridiculously expensive stables – for that was exactly what they still looked like, despite the central heating and all mod. cons. It did not take me long to accept the fact that this was a wasted journey.

There was a train back to London from Tunbridge Wells in less than half an hour and I decided to take a taxi to the Central Station. As we swung out of Fordcombe village I happened to get chatting to the taxi-driver about local place names.

'I suppose,' I ventured, 'you know everywhere around here.'

'As a matter of fact,' he replied, 'I thought I did until a week ago. Then someone asked me to take him to Earwig Green. And that had me proper stumped.'

'To where?' I inquired incredulously.

'Earwig Green. It isn't on the map, leastways no map I've ever seen. Not even a hamlet, just a group of cottages.'

'Is it far?' I asked, a mad idea surging up inside me.

'About a mile, no more.'

'Then let's go there. I'd like to see what such a place looks like.'

He swivelled round in his seat and regarded me with profound suspicion.

'It's going to cut it a bit fine for your train, sir, if we do.'

'To hell with my train. Earwig Green sounds a better proposition than Fordcombe.'

So to Earwig Green we went. It really does exist and about one in three taxi-drivers in Tunbridge Wells, I have since found out, knows his way there. Well, this fanciful site was not in the least impressive, but I still had a feeling of being the discoverer of something important. It was one of those inexplicably elated feelings that sometimes compensate for a disappointment: I knew that Earwig Green was the clue to something.

Perhaps it was the lovely evening – still, warm and bathed in a golden-yellow light which played tricks with the trees. The countryside was lush and silent: we were well off the main road. The taxi-man and I looked for a pub. I think he was as thirsty as I was and it was close on opening time. But, alas, the taxi-man had only been to Earwig Green once in his life before and he knew as little about the local geography as I did. And there was no one in sight to direct us to wherever we might quench our nicotine-dried tongues.

'We'd better be getting back, sir. There's barely time to catch your train.'

'Well, forget it. My thirst is more important.'

'You can get a nice drink in Tunbridge Wells.'

'Maybe, but I want a country pub, not a spa lounge.'

'Well, we could go back to Fordcombe.'

'I never believe in going back on my tracks. It's more fun exploring. Anyhow, we must find a pub soon.'

Resignedly the taxi-man got back in his car and somewhat hesitantly drove off down a side-road. For five miles we ran sweetly along a winding, pine-sheltered lane. But still there was no pub in sight.

'Funny,' mused the taxi-man, 'but I do believe I've got you lost. I could have sworn this lane led on to the Flimwell road. We must be well into Sussex now. Tell you what, I'll turn left at the end here and that should bring us back on to the Flimwell road.'

But it didn't. The left-hand turn continued almost full circle until we were heading in the same direction as before. Suddenly a sign-post appeared round a corner. We pulled up sharply to read it and there, boldly and clearly imprinted, were the words 'CODIHAM I MILE'.

Codiham? Where had I heard that name before? For a while the coincidence escaped me. Then I recollected the cutting which Sylvia had given me months previously. Turning out my pockets, I found it and read again:

'Less well known is the MERRY DAMSEL at Codiham. . . .'

'Do you know Codiham?' I asked the taxi-man.

'I've heard of it. Bit outside my normal area. You see, sir, this is Sussex, and I don't often venture this way. Also Codiham is not the sort of place people often go to.'

This sounded even more promising.

'Well, I'll tell you something,' said I, triumphantly. 'Codiham has a pub. A pub with an enormous round bed in it. It's called the Merry Damsel and that's where you and I are now going.'

'Good God, sir! You know more about these parts than I do. Merry what did you say?'

'Damsel.'

'Well, it's a name you can't easily forget. Merry Damson, eh? Let's hope it is merry, for this little trip is going to cost you a pretty packet, I'm afraid. And what's this ruddy bed you are talking about?'

'You'll see. And it's Damsel, not Damson, by the way.'

'It all sounds pretty dam' silly to me,' retorted the taxi-man, his gears grinding into action as we turned into the Codiham road.

2. 'Us be proper wicked down at Codgem'

AFTER Plush, Ryme Intrinsica, Lovelands and Sinwell, Codiham, to the uncultured townsman's ear, at first sounded rather a let-down.

I was swiftly educated on the subject. When I referred to 'Co-di-ham', the taxi-man gazed at me scornfully and said: 'I thought you knew all about this place. If you start talking about Co-di-ham round here no one will understand you. Codgem, that's what the locals call it. Much easier than trying to get your tongue round all three syllables, isn't it?'

I must confess I was rather pleased at this piece of information. The homely and plebian 'Codgem' seemed much more euphonious than my precise, unlovely attempt at pronunciation.

Codiham is not a set-piece, a picture-book village that suddenly appears round a corner. True, it is tucked away in a clearing in the woods, but it makes itself known by a delicate and leisurely strip-tease act, discarding its leafy garments and revealing its charms gradually. The effectiveness of Codiham lies in its splendid confusion of the homely and the beautiful, the unusual and the placidly normal, of country innocence and rustic guile. It is – or shall I say she is? – a damsel completely oblivious of the impression she makes, so coy that as you approach the village from the tree-lined lane, you see nothing of her for half a mile. Away beyond the woods, to the north, is a high ridge of hills which shelters the Weald as it billows down in great waves of green and chalk foam before merging with the deeper green of forest and orchard land. Then, a mere pin-point at first, the pinnacled tower of Codiham Church comes into view, set like a sentinel above the oaks, beeches and elms. Grey-stoned and battlemented, its four octagonal corner-turrets and tapering steeple lend a majesty which neither sun, nor gloom can erase.

Admittedly the tower and steeple seem far too large for the actual church, which is squat, humble and patched. But I shall not easily forget the effect Codiham Church first had upon me – not that of an all-enveloping Protestant greyness and sobriety, but of a glowing torch of eternal triumph over the centuries as the sun painted its corner-turrets with pink and the steeple-top with gold.

A clearing in the woods gleamed with yellow-and-red broom and the evening light bathed the pines in its warmth; we turned sharp left into a narrow road of rag-stone cottages with neatly trimmed, tiny lawns and sprucely tailored hedges. Each little cottage garden had something unusual in it . . . a beehive here, a ship's figurehead there, a splash of roses in one minute plot and a lily pond in another. There was a cluster of oast houses and the strange, bitter-sweet tang of hops. Within a few minutes we were in the heart of the village.

At first I didn't realize this was the centre of Codiham. Again that demure damsel hid from one the last few charms she had to reveal. My impression was of a large triangular green and masses of trees. Then, as I got out of the taxi, and peered more intently across the green, I saw that it was completely ringed by poplars and beeches, oaks and elms. These could not obscure the church tower and steeple, but momentarily they masked the three main streets of Codiham which are also the three sides of the triangular green.

Peeping through the trees on the farther sides of the green I saw in superb disarray an assortment of Tudor shop-fronts, black-and-white gabled houses, Queen Anne and Georgian cottages and a seventeenth-century red-brick mansion tucked away behind massive iron gates.

Codiham is not a village you can quickly sum up. There is nothing planned about it. Even the village green is an uneven jungle of grass and trees, only its tiny cricket pitch lending a hint of order and this smooth, velvet paradise for the batsman, the product of more than a hundred years' mowing and rolling, swiftly descends into an outfield of rhododendron bushes.

This was about as much as I was able to take in as we drew up outside the Merry Damsel. And, if you go to Codiham for the first time and catch sight of the sign of the Merry Damsel, I am willing to bet you won't take in anything else for several minutes. The inn sign completely dominates the hostelry. It is far too large for the inn itself and has an odd touch of modernity in a framework of intricate wrought iron-work, the product of seventeenth-century craftsmen. The iron-work is, indeed, the only ancient thing about this extraordinary sign with its bold, almost frighteningly photographic painting of a full-bosomed Restoration belle smiling down at one as she sits up in an enormous bed.

'Blimey!' said the taxi-driver, who was one of those half-cockney, half-countrymen who so often haunt the larger towns of Kent. 'Blimey!' he said again. 'So you weren't kidding about a bed. Say, is this popsy still alive?'

'Dead some two hundred and fifty years, I fancy. But we should be able to find out all about her when we go inside.'

'Bet she looks smashing when she's floodlit.'

There was no time to stop and admire the rambling, black-beamed exterior of the inn with its mullioned windows and gay striped canopies of red and white. We made straight for the public bar for the simple reason that this is the best place in which to judge any tavern and, secondly, it is more likely to provide a truer picture of a village.

It was not one's idea of a conventional public bar; it was half tap-room, half-parlour, with a little 'snug' leading off it. The barrels, immaculate in their red-and-white piped covers, lay invitingly in a cool corner of the tap; brass and copper trays and pans winked in the cool, mellow gloom that those in the public bar seem to prefer. One's main impression was of a gathering of people who had already settled down for the night. The atmosphere was not of a place where a few persons have popped in for a quick one, but rather of a club whose members intend staying until closing time. A game of cribbage was in progress in one corner; two men were playing darts, while the rest were comfortably ensconced in a large recess round the open fireplace, pints of beer in massive tankards, firmly grasped. A winter's night habit, no doubt, continued in summer.

No one spoke as the taxi-driver and I went up to the bar counter, but I was conscious of the fact that we were both being carefully inspected and probably put on trial.

A rotund, middle-aged figure with cheeks like russet apples waddled up to the counter and asked us what 'our pleasure' was. I liked that phrase and warmed to the man at once.

'Two pints of your very best bitter,' I replied.

He was not one to let a chance of salesmanship slip was the rotund one.

'Certainly, sir. You said "very best bitter". I wonder would you like to try a drop of our October Ale, sir. It's a heavy gravity beer and, though they do say as how you should only drink it in winter, I reckon it's a lovely drink any time.'

'We'll take your advice,' said I.

'I knew there was summat odd about this village,' commented the taxi-driver lugubriously. 'October Ale! You never hear of that in Tunbridge Wells.'

We drank copiously at first, then settled down to sip the heady, potent brew. It was rather like the famous Audit Ales which used to be – and may still be, for all I know – brewed at Trinity College, Cambridge. Meanwhile, the barman gave us the benefit of a running commentary on the merits of different beers and ales.

'You'll get no refrigerated muck in this house,' he advised. 'Terrible, these newfangled cellars with their iced beer and their American notions. Now, myself, gentlemen, I'm a beer man, born and bred on it. Bitter, yes; old and mild for a morning session, but give me a pint of real old ale at night. And this October stuff, it's worth every penny.

'Now the guvnor here likes 'is spirits and knows 'is wines. But he never forgets that it's beer that kept this house goin' for centuries, and it bein' a free house, he takes the trouble to give the beer man as wide a choice as possible.

'But these moderns they don't know nothin' about beer,' he added, polishing glasses with astonishing speed for one so slow in his movements. 'Now most mild and bitter today is round about one thousand and thirty Original Gravity, but this strong stuff is nearer one thousand two hundred. Makes you think, doesn't it?'

'Not 'alf,' replied the taxi-man. 'I reckon I'll do well to steer a straight course on my way home. And by the way, sir, are you ready to be getting along, or will you have one more of these October Ales in flaming July?'

'I'll answer your second question first. I'll have half a pint with you. As to whether I'm coming, that rather depends on our friend here.'

'On me, sir?' inquired the rotund one.

'Yes. I'm beginning to like this ale. But, if I'm to go on drinking it I must know whether you can put me up for the night.'

'Ah, sir, you'll have to see the landlord about that. We don't do much trade in the week here, so I should think it ud be all right. Wait a moment and I'll 'ave a word with 'im. Was it bed and breakfast you was wanting?'

'Dinner, if you do it, bed and breakfast,' I added.

'Proper made up yer mind for a night out, 'aven't yer?' said the taxi-man.

'I don't know about a night out, but I certainly want to see a bit more of this village.'

'Well, you won't see it if you stay in here. At the rate you're sinking those October Ales, I doubt, sir, whether you'll see yer way upstairs at closing time.'

.   .   .   .   .

The taxi-man was paid and had departed, wishing me luck, and, judging by his look, doubting whether I'd have it. The rotund one whose name he informed me was 'Young George' ('I've bin 'ere since I was fifteen, first as boots, then in the bar and I'm still "Young George" to all of 'em in 'ere'), told me it was all right about the bed and that if I cared to pop into the saloon I could order my dinner.

'Here's to Codgem!' said I, putting back my fourth October Ale.

'Bless you, sir, if you ain't got the name spoke right first time. That's more 'an most of 'em can do.'

'Tell me,' I said, 'who is the saucy puss who gives one the glad eye from your inn sign?'

'Oh, that's our Miranda, the pride and the shame of all Codgem, sir. Yes, Miranda's the girl who brings 'em in 'ere, the wickedest little puss in all Sussex.'

'Of course, I've heard all about the King's Damsel's Bed. Tell me, is that where I sleep?'

Young George puffed out his ruddy cheeks and spluttered with uncontrollable laughter. 'Oh, sir, you'll be the death of me! If you got in that bed by yourself, you'd be like a traveller lost in the Saharee. It's that big, you'd die of loneliness.'

'But do people sleep in it?'

Young George bent down close to my face and whispered confidentially: 'Well, there are folks as tries to persuade the landlord to let 'em try. I reckon they're unmarried couples out for a dirty week-end and think a big bed will give 'em more scope. But we don't encourage such notions, not even in wicked Codgem, we don't. Mind you, I have known people sleep in it. On very special terms and for very distinguished guests, begging your pardon, sir, it can be done. There was one French Ambassador who called in here one day and he got the bed by special request. But, bless you, sir, wot could you expect from a Froggie?'

'Was he alone?'

'Wot, a Froggie alone? Not on yet bloomin' life, 'ee weren't.'

'It costs a pretty packet to sleep in the celebrated King's Damsel's Bed, does it?'

'Ah, that depends on the landlord, sir. But we don't get ambassadors staying 'ere every night and when they do, well, we charges for the privilege, as you might say.'

'Just now, George, you talked about wicked Codgem. What did you mean?'

'Oh, that. Well, it's a saying we 'ave locally – "Us be proper wicked down at Codgem." You'll hear 'em say it if you stop here long enough.'

'And why should you be "proper wicked" at Codgem?'

'Well, I reckon in Codgem, unlike lots of Sussex villages, we 'ave more'n a sense of 'umour than most. We can laugh at ourselves in Codgem surelye,[1] that's as how we keeps so cheerful. 'aven't you noticed that, sir?'

'They seem cheerful enough in here,' I replied, noting the steady hum of conversation in the tap-room and the revelry when a treble top was scored at darts.

'Dunnamany[2] how many years the saying goes back. But there was a squire in Codgem and they do say as how he was a cannibal. In a way of speaking he liked 'is 'uman flesh, so much so that he paid large sums of money for any unwanted babies – and there's allus bin plenty of 'em in Codgem – for his supper of a night. Well, this squire chappie gave us a proper bad name. In other parts of Sussex they used to talk about "those cannibals at Codgem". Just as if we was all as fond of 'uman flesh as the squire.'

'And so?'

'That all started it. You see, though we wasn't all cannibals at Codgem, we was rather a bad lot. There was Miranda on our inn sign. She's the Merry Damsel, of course. Well, it was in this famous bed that she and old Charlie the Second romped and a gentleman like you, sir, will know what a proper terror 'ee was with the ladies. That's why they called her the King's Damsel.

---

[1] *Surelye* is a commonly used Sussex word with no particular meaning other than to give emphasis.

[2] *Dunnamany* means 'I don't know how many'.

'But she was only one of many damsels. We still call a saucy puss a damsel down at Codgem. In the Puritans' days they used to duck 'em in the pond on Cucking Green.'

'I didn't see any pond.'

'No. Happen you didn't come that way. It's on the far side of the Green from here. You must see it and our swans. The Green is called "Cooking Green" by us locals, but it's spelt C-U-C-K-I-N-G Green. The pond used to be an old hammer pond and that's where Codgem's bad girls and nagging wives used to be ducked from the cucking-stool.

'Yes, they did say as how Codgem was the worst spot in all Sussex for girls who went cucking – not quite what you might think it is, if you don't mind me saying so, sir. "Cucking" is, well, an old local love-making pastime. You'll hear about that, too, if you stays on. Oh, yes, in bygone days – and quite a bit now for that matter, with all these Teddy boys and girls – there was cucking and kissing and bussing on Cucking Green of a night. Then this used to be the centre for bear-baiting and cock-fighting, not to mention the smugglers who organized the traffic in brandy and silks between Rye and London. And all that gave us a worse name. So, just to laugh it off like the sportsmen we are in these parts, we grinned and replied: "Us be proper wicked down at Codgem." '

'Well, I'm all for a spot of wickedness if it gives colour and character to a place,' I added. 'Between you and me, I'm looking for a village to live in. Do you think they'd have me here, George? Am I wicked enough? And what are the chances of finding a place?'

George looked serious and pondered a moment. 'I think they might get used to you, sir. 'Course, I wouldn't deny we're a conservative lot in Codgem and many of 'em still look on strangers as furriners – even if they only crosses the border from Hawkhurst in Kent. But that sort of attitude is passing now that we've got the telly. And there's one advantage: as a furriner you dursn't 'ave to be wicked, only tolerant. But what worries me is where you could find a place to live. Was it for yourself alone, or a family, sir?'

'Wife and one small son.'

'Tom!' shouted Young George across the tap-room to one of the beer drinkers round the hearth. 'Tom, do you know of any house or cottage wot's for sale in Codgem?'

Tom, a rheumy septuagenarian, took his pipe from his mouth, spat reflectively and replied slowly: 'There's that house at Six Elms. It's bin up for sale purty near a twelve month.'

'Ah, they wants too much for un,' chipped in his companion. 'Four thousand and dry rot thrown in.'

'Now, don't you be getting slanderous, not in this bar,' urged Young George.

''oose talking about slander? I only gave the gentleman sound advice. What about that tumbledown cottage t'other side of the Green? It's a bargain at eight hundred pounds and old Jo Simcox ud thatch un in no time at all.'

In a short while I was inundated with offers . . . the house with dry rot at Six Elms, a tumbledown cottage and a converted piggery. None of them seemed promising and the idea of coping with the thatching of a tumbledown cottage presented a searing nightmare, despite the fact that I was assured 'old Joe Simcox' was the finest thatcher in two counties. But Young George promised that, while I was having dinner, he would make a few more 'discreet inquiries'.

'So don't you worry, sir. We'll find you summat.'

.   .   .   .   .

Externally there is nothing remarkable about the Merry Damsel save for its sign and portrait of the lovely Miranda. It is just one of many ancient inns with its red-tiled roof and its black timber. But, as you leave the tap-room and enter the lobby, history swiftly unfolds itself.

Here in the lobby is something of many different centuries. The beams must surely date back to at least 1550, but the panelling, divided into squares in each of which is carved an oak apple, is certainly of a much later date, while the brasses and the carved cherubs around the cocktail bar, with the gilded Italianate imagery on the pillars, are evidence of eighteenth-century influences. Framed on the wall is what is described as 'A Sussex Version of the Song of Solomon', by Mark Antony Lower:

'Lookee, you be purty, my love. You've got dove's eyes adin yer locks; yer hair is like a flock of goats dat appear from Mount Gilead.

Yer teeth be lik a flock of ship just shared, dat come up from de ship-wash; every one of em bears tweens, and nare a one among em is barren.

Yer lips be lik a thread of scarlet, an yer speech is comely; yer temples be lik a bit of pomegranate adin yer locks.

Yer nick is lik de tower of Daoved, built for an armoury, what dey heng a thousan bucklers on, all shields of mighty men.

Yer two breasts be lik two young roses, what be tweens, dat feed among de lilies.

You be hem purty, my love, der aunt a spot in ye.

How much better is yer love dan wine! an de smell of yer garments dan all spices.

Wake, O north win, an come, ye south, blow upon my garn, dat de spices of it may flow out. Let me beloved come into his garn, an ait his pleasant fruits.'

Doubtless the lovely Miranda would have understood this language – probably far better than the sophisticated compliments of Charles II, for another framed parchment proclaimed that 'Miranda Puttock, the King's Damsel, was Sussex born and bred. She was the daughter of Isaac Puttock, landlord of the Merry Damsel, born at Codiham in 1652, died in the same place 1698.'

Still musing on the fair Miranda, I walked into the long, low dining-room, my mind more on an ancient love than on food. It was a pleasant, silent room, surrounded with linen-fold panelling, the ceiling a forest of great oak beams, blackened by time and smoke; through the open windows came the scent of roses, wafted up from the inn's garden, which was profusely colourful and carved out round a tiny courtyard in which grew a fig-tree.

A tall, dark, rather pallid man approached with a smile of welcome. It was rather an anxious smile, as though he had a major task to fulfil and was not quite sure whether I would co-operate. But this in itself was more comforting than the normal, artificial grin of the head waiter who has one eye on the next table.

'I thought you would like to know that it's quite all right about your room, sir. You have no luggage, I believe.'

'No, I – er – well, I just decided to stop on the spur of the moment. Perhaps in the circumstances you would like me to pay for the room now.'

'Not at all. I was wondering whether there was anything you might want. I think we might be able to lend you shaving gear, or a brush and comb.'

'That's very kind of you. I ought to explain that this is quite a chance visit to Codiham. Quite illogical, I know, but I have taken a fancy to it and thought I'd stay on and have a look round.'

'Codiham is a little off the map, perhaps. Not on the main road. But probably all the better for that, though we don't get the same trade as some villages.'

'I suppose you don't cater much for casual diners like myself.'

'Oh, indeed, we try to do our best. One never knows. At week-ends we are often quite full, especially in summer. Fishermen and a few golfers, you know. Both are exceedingly food-minded and have tremendous appetites. But it is difficult to cater during the week, as some nights we may only have two or three people in to dinner. But we try to keep a few surprises up our sleeves. What would you like to begin with? Scampi Francis? Or our own rather special Rye Bay Relish; it's really a fish hors d'œuvre of prawns, sole cooked in cider, with a cheese sauce, a very old Sussex recipe which I found in an old handwritten cookery book in the cellars. And after that I could offer you veal cutlets and mushrooms, or carpet-bag steak.'

It sounded wonderful. It was wonderful. Devoted as I am to scampi, I couldn't resist the Rye Bay Relish, washed down, at a wise landlord's suggestion, not with hock, or white Bordeaux, but a glass of that superb vintage cider which Sussex produces of a quality that has the lightness of a French white wine, the sweetness of a light Spanish wine and the potency and some of the flavour of Calvados. How good it was to be away from the pretensions of bogus gourmets and wine experts, how soothing to find a landlord who abolished French words from the menu of an essentially English inn. The Rye Bay Relish was cooked in cider, so what could be more appropriate than to drink cider with it? And this was cider which sparkled as elegantly and as clearly in a slender glass as any hock, or sauterne.

By the time I had started on the veal cutlets and mushrooms, I was ready for another glass of the vintage cider, and this time I asked for a whole bottle. And it was then, as I removed the heart-shaped paper-cases from the veal cutlets that I began to feel that on a Wednesday night Codiham belonged to me. This, I kept telling myself, was it. The problem was how to convince the family and how to find a home here. But that could wait.

The landlord of the Merry Damsel was one of those dedicated men to whom inn-keeping was the greatest thing which life had to offer. In France such dedication can make a man a vast fortune; in England, if he refuses to lower his standards, he may be lucky if he breaks even. He was landlord, part-chef (with his wife's assistance), head-waiter and receptionist. How he managed to cope with all these tasks with such equanimity, I don't know, but I fancy the anxious smile revealed that it was a labour of love. His name was Pargetter; his father had had the inn before him and his grandfather before that. That in itself explained the devotion to Sussex fare and drink, the refusal to have French on his menus (all written out in ink by himself): 'they would never stand for it in Codgem, sir. Not that *they* ever dine here; they stay in the tap-room. But they would think I was giving myself airs and that would never do.'

He had, however, travelled far and wide and broadened his outlook on inn-keeping. 'The great thing is to feel an inn is your home. To switch from one house to another, to be always on the move is no way for an inn-keeper to live. He must have roots.'

'But you have managed to introduce some touches which are not purely Sussex?' I queried.

'You mean the rose-petal decorations on the tables? That is my wife's idea. We have small dining-tables and a bowl of flowers either drops petals in the soup, or obscures the view. Golfers hate them. My wife is French. Took a long time for the villagers to get used to her nationality. But, being French, she is not only a natural cook and a thrifty housewife, but she hates extravagance. Fresh-cut flowers, she decided, were a waste on the dining-room tables, so she always utilizes the petals of flowers in season to make her ornamental patterns on the tables.'

Mr. Pargetter had spent a year in France, gaining experience: 'I worked as a waiter for a whole year and it taught me a great deal about the English which I didn't know before. It taught me that, whereas they would turn up their noses at skate in their own country, they would gladly eat it under the name of *raie* in France.

'Whose idea was the inn-sign?' I asked.

'That, I am afraid, was my one concession to the new age. It seemed rather silly not to advertise the inn's historical links. Of course, not everyone holds with the inn-sign in Codiham,' he added wistfully. 'Yet it's the work of a local artist and it's a good thing that inn-signs are coming back into favour. Before the war there was just the wrought-iron framework and a tattered-creaking board with the words "Merry Damsel" on it. That picture of Miranda may be rather controversial; they still talk about it in the tap-room. But it is in the spirit of the place.'

'This saying here,' I said. ' "Us be proper wicked down at Codgem." Don't they think the inn-sign rather makes sense of that saying?'

He smiled. 'Ah, yes, but the Puritan spirit lingers on in Codgem. Smuggling and nonconformity, you know, went hand in hand, and the nonconformity lives on. There are all manner of peculiar sects round here. And if it isn't the nonconformists, the Teddy boys take a hand. They pelted Miranda with rotten tomatoes one night.'

Sensibly there was no other light than that of candles in the dining-room. They cast a carnival flicker over the *Surprise Miranda*, a rum-baked soufflé which lay deceptively warmly on what was a heart-shaped lemon-ice. Did Miranda really have a heart so chill, I wondered. The home-brewed cherry brandy, thicker and more syrupy than most of its kind, made me doubt it.

3. *Partly about hops*

WHEN I finished my dinner I realized with a shock that it was now nine o'clock and that I should have been home half an hour before. I must telephone my wife and explain my wanderings. But before doing this I wanted at least to have some excuse, some hint of a house for sale, or a piggery that might be converted.

I returned to the tap-room and Young George said he had been making inquiries and would I care to go down the road to the Bearpits. If I did, and asked for 'Sailor' Thompsett, he might help; if I didn't find him in the Bearpits, *surelye* he would be in the Hole in the Wall. 'He keeps reg'lar pub hours, does "Sailor". Tomorrow night 'ee's allus here – prompt at opening time for the slate club. Stays till nigh on ten, then goes to the Hole in the Wall for a binder. Other nights you'll allus see him in the Bearpits or the Hole. And "Sailor" knows everything what goes on round Codgem. If anyone can fix you up, it 'ull be him. Tom says doan't 'ee go chasin' up that converted piggery; it bain't fit for pigs, 'ee says.'

October Ale, vintage cider and afterwards rough draught cider at the Bearpits had begun to take toll of me. My head was clear, but my walk was like a roll. The Bearpits was a further reminder of Codiham's 'wickedness'; it was a public house built on the site of the former bear-baiting pits when Codiham was the centre of a prosperous Wealden trade. But today there is nothing more dashing than marbles beds in the courtyards and 'bull and ring' played in the public bar.

'Sailor' Thompsett wasn't there. He had left 'not more'n a couple of beers ago'. They count time in terms of beer in Codiham. Off I went, still rolling somewhat, to the Hole in the Wall, which, as you might expect from such a name, was not easy to find. It is the smallest pub in Codiham, built into a large, windowless wall, on the other side of which is a disused quay which looks out on to the partly silted up River Dentical, another odd local name derived from the old Sussex word for 'dainty'. The 'Dainty River' and, indeed, dainty she is, as, twisting this way and that in a narrow channel, like a slim, silvery eel, she threads her way through woods and meadowland down towards the sea. Three centuries ago boats came up the Dentical laden with timber for the Codiham saw-mills; then the Hole in the Wall must have been a prosperous hostelry, and undoubtedly the headquarters for the Codiham Gang of smugglers. But today only an occasional fisherman wends his way up here from the coast, bringing with him Rye Bay plaice, dabs and, occasionally, crustacean delicacies.

Eventually, in the middle of that wall I found 'The Hole'; it was little more than a door set well back and low down, reached by three well-worn steps. One walked straight down into a kind of cellar, cool and smelling richly of beer and tobacco. The walls were covered with a vast variety of what can only be called nostalgic mementoes . . . old ship's badges, fishing-nets, a score of picture postcards stuck on a plaque, visiting-cards and sporting prints had been fastened to the ceiling; there were faded, yellow portraits of the trousered, whiskered footballers of eighty years ago. There was no semblance of a bar, only beer barrels for tables and the same 'furniture', suitably polished, served for chairs.

In the garish light of naked electric light bulbs I discerned through the haze of blue smoke a motley gathering of what I presumed were Codiham's most devil-may-care inhabitants. If the Merry Damsel was the aristocrat of the village, there was little doubt that the Hole in the Wall was its Robespierre, its radical revolutionary, hell-bent hive of rumbustious, fanatical gaiety. I repeat, *fanatical* gaiety. There was no mistaking the fierce sounds not only of mirth, but of those who would damn you eternally if you were not equally full of mirth. A long face would probably have produced a murder in the Hole in the Wall; certainly no sad man dare enter its portals and emerge unscathed verbally. Luckily I was already merry.

As I have said, there was no bar. That, I think, is the vital factor in making this tiny pub (with no nonsense about having a snug, or a saloon) such an uninhibited place. The barrels of mild and bitter were within reach of all; nothing would have been easier than to have turned the tap and helped oneself. It had no wine and spirit licence and was essentially a beer house, with rough cider thrown in for good measure. And, presiding over it all, was the buxom, flaming red-head whom everyone seemed to be calling Flossie.

'Look wot's walked in, Flossie,' cried a bucolic, heavy-lidded chap who eyed me with the gravest doubts. 'Must be one of them Government fellows.'

'Government fellows? Well, wot of it?' inquired the good-natured Flossie, winking at me. 'I reckon the gentleman's just come to take a good look at the zoo. Good evenin', sir, and what can I do for you?'

I added that she could do me for a pint of bitter. I hadn't the nerve to ask for less for fear of being damned for ever. I had already noticed that in Codiham one drank pints, never half-pints.

Flossie soon bustled up with a foaming pint and begged me to 'find a seat, if you can'.

'Before I sit down,' I said, 'there's someone I'm trying to find. "Sailor" Thompsett is the name.'

A loud guffaw echoed through the cellar bar.

'Ooaah! After you agin, "Sailor". Better come quietly like to the gentleman,' chortled another ruffianly looking character who might have been a fisherman, or a Chelsea artist trying to be rustic.

And forward came 'Sailor', striding across the cellar with a nautical swagger, a broad grin on his scarred and weather-beaten face, his clay pipe sticking out of his mouth at a rakish angle. There was no mistaking that 'Sailor' Thompsett was a man of the sea; his dark blue jersey with a skull and crossbones worked on the front in white wool were not necessary for one to deduce this; nor was the brass ear-ring he affected on his left ear.

'And wot can I do for you, comrade?'

'Take no notice of 'im, sir. 'ee calls us all comrades. Proper Bolshie is our "Sailor" when 'ee likes.'

'Young George at the Merry Damsel sent me to see you. Said you might know of a cottage, or a house that might be up for sale.'

'Sailor' scratched his head. He grinned approvingly at Flossie: 'Allus know where to get the truth, doan't they, Flossie, my luv? Come to old "Sailor" and 'ee'l tell 'ee. Well, comrade, sir, they're not many properties agoin' in these parts – not anything worth 'aving. And when we 'ears of 'em, they generally gets snapped up locally. We doan't 'ave much truck with furriners down at Codgem.'

Flossie looked shocked at such forthright statements.

'No, I understand that,' I replied. 'I gathered you're a pretty wicked lot.'

There was a hoot of merriment. 'Danged if he ain't got us summed up already,' said one.

'You'll do for Codgem,' added another.

'Are you wicked, too comrade?' asked 'Sailor'. 'If so, happen as we could do summat for yer. But you woan't find no easy livin' in Codgem, no luxury houses, or any of that lark. But if you is prepared to take it tough and set about makin' a home for yersel', well, I reckon we might 'ave a tip or two. Would you be prepared to chance yer luck on an oast house?'

Now I did recognize an oast house when I saw one. I knew vaguely that in such a place the hops were dried over a fire. But the idea of actually living in one of these conical oddities had never occurred to me.

'All depends on what can be done with it.'

'Well, I'll tell yer. T'other side of Cucking Green, between Mad Miranda's place and the church there's a disused oast. It's bin derelict for years, ever since 1939 leastways. Now it ain't much to look at, but it's solid, well built and nothing really wrong with it. You could turn it into quite a cosy home. Just think, walls a foot thick – keep you as quiet as in a cathedral, snug in winter and cool in summer. And remember, with round rooms, you get no draughts. Cost you six hundred quid. Yer might 'ave to spend several hundreds on it, but it 'ud be worth it, every penny of it. What do you say?'

I can't remember much more that night. There was a round of drinks with 'Sailor', who insisted on buying a round back, a round with two other fellows and a farewell drink with Flossie before we all tipsily staggered off to view the derelict oast house in the moonlight. It looked gaunt, ghostly and full of decay in a wilderness of weed . . . nettles, dandelions, thistles, rotting black currant bushes and masses of sodden timber. Yet, in the moonlight, it had a certain poetry; the tall, conical roof, the swinging white cowl gave it the appearance of an unsinkable old galleon.

'I'll take it,' I said, rashly, adding a conventional caution to my quixotry by mentioning 'subject, of course, to the survey'.

'Grand,' replied 'Sailor'. 'I'll see you in the tap-room of the Merry Damsel tomorrow morning at eleven and take you to meet the agent. Don't worry about the survey. There's no dry rot in an oast, nor wood-worm either. Maybe there's a lot to be done to it, but you'll never regret your choice.'

And that was that. Somehow I found my way back to the Merry Damsel, thanks to a now flood-lit Miranda, mine host's one concession to modernity. I made a telephone call to my wife, over which I had best draw a veil. There was no disguising the fact that I was in a pleasantly maudlin state of mind and the situation was in no manner improved by the fact that the telephone call woke up my young son to whom I unwisely said: 'Tell your mother I've found an oast house.'

To which he excitedly shouted out: 'Mummy, Daddy has found a ghost house.'

It is an odd thing that whereas wives rather expect husbands to err when abroad, they are much more exacting in their standards of propriety when in this country. Had we been in the Wicked City, Sylvia might have taken it all for granted. But she found it hard to believe I had found a 'Wicked Village' in the Sussex Weald and my repetitive 'Us be proper wicked down at Codgem', punctuated by gurgles of lunatic laughter, hardly helped matters. I am still not sure whether she thought I'd found an oast house or a 'ghost house' that night, but fortunately for me a fairly tolerant voice tartly suggested I had best go straight to bed.

Which I did. And I made another surprising discovery. Young George showed me up to my room and with that Rabelaisian belly laugh of his guffawed: 'We put you up for the night in Jezebel. We allus gives this room to unaccompanied gentlemen. You see, sir, in the Merry Damsel, we durst not number the rooms, we names 'em.'

There were six bedrooms at the Merry Damsel – three doubles and three singles – and the names were Jezebel, Old Rowley, Marigold, the Folly (an attic room in the Doric manner), the Priest's Hole (an alleged former secret hiding-place), the Look-out (which had a magnificent view across the Weald). Miranda's Room, in which was the famous Bed, was not counted as a normal bedroom, but rather as a museum piece.

But the last-named I was not to see that night. For my own part I went to bed in Pepysian mood to sleep off my October Ale in a four-poster.

Why is it that a 'morning after' in England is so much more marked by remorse and misgivings than a similar state of mind in any other part of the world?

It may be that we never quite escape from our Puritan past in England, that, whatever our transgressions, however much we have warmed to Bacchus the night before, a Milton, or a Bunyan is there to shriek retribution in the morning. It matters not if the morning be of winter or summer, if the cuckoo mocks, or a nor'-easter roars: the immediate consequence of waking up is to come face to face with Reality in his many obscene disguises.

As I turned over uneasily in the four-poster, I found it hard to realize where I was. I knew I had been drinking October Ale in midsummer, that I had added to this devilish brew vintage cider, draught cider and innumerable bitters. But what else had I done? Then I dimly remembered having more or less agreed to buy an oast house.

The recollection filled me with dismay. I knew next to nothing about oast houses and even less about buildings generally. When it comes to inspecting a property I am the complete clot, clueless and gormless. I am clay in the hands of preying estate agents and would-be vendors. Even if I knew how to detect dry rot, even if I knew one ought to demand 'access to the roof', or to probe the drainage, I should never dream of casting any such aspersion on the place I was viewing. To me there is something uncivilized and nasty about a prospective buyer who prods and probes, who asks awkward and rude questions. I know this is utterly illogical, but I can't help it.

I breakfasted well. There was mine host, Pargetter, still dark and pallid – suitably so for my peace of mind – fully realizing the urgent need for silence at the breakfast table. There, too, was his French wife, affable, but not attempting conversation, deftly conjuring up rashers of ham and eggs and crisp toast with a copious pot of soothing coffee. Through the window came the scent of roses and the sounds of a cooing dove; sanity surged back into my veins, uncongealed by my cursory glance at the morning paper which Pargetter laid in front of me.

Pargetter was a wonder. Had he made such a gesture at night, I should have regarded him as a phoney, but when, teaspoon in one hand and a bottle of Armagnac in the other, he quietly offered: 'May I spoil your coffee, sir?' I could have awarded him the sash of a *Cordon Bleu* on the spot.

I did not need to do more than murmur my thanks as the teaspoonful of precious brandy was gently tipped into the steaming, brown-black liquid in my cup. Pargetter knew and I knew that this was the turning point in my day. That teaspoonful of brandy in the coffee was not the hair of the dog that had bitten me, but the sweet dispensation of an all-seeing Father Confessor.

'Did you have any luck last night, sir?' asked Pargetter when my breakfast was finished.

'I seem to remember having been sold an oast house.'

'Ah, that would be the old oast on the other side of the Green, facing the pond. You would have a nice view of the swans there.'

'Is it worth buying, do you think?'

'I think something could be done with it. What price was asked?'

'Six hundred.'

'Well, I mustn't commit myself. But I'd say it was a reasonable proposition. Your real problem will be how much to spend on converting it. And if I may say so, you ought to get expert advice on that.'

'Thanks. You've told me a great deal in a few words. But I think my real problem is going to be selling the idea to the rest of my family. They hardly know what an oast house looks like.'

I met 'Sailor' Thompsett in the tap-room; he took me round to see the agent and I duly wrote out a cheque for £60 as a deposit on the derelict oast. Then I returned to Ealing to make my peace.

It is, perhaps, worth while saying a few words about oast houses. Unless you can visualize the historic background to these cone-roofed oddities dotted about East Sussex and Kent, the romance of an oast house is completely lost. In fact, unless you really appreciate what went on in an oast before you live in one, its significance is no greater than that of a semi-detached in Surbiton.

About 1524 the hop plant was introduced to England from the continent of Europe. It was not at first received with any sense of gratitude. Vested interests combined to make hostile propaganda against 'this heathen weed', or *humulus lupulus*, as it is technically known. But, gradually, despite all this antagonism, public opinion insisted that hops were an entirely desirable commodity and they were grown in most of the home counties. The year 1524 must have been a memorable one in social history, if one judges it by the ancient rhyme:

> Turkeys, carps, hoppes, piccavel and beer
> Came into England all in one year.

But it was the rich soil of the Weald in East Sussex and Kent which swiftly proved to be by far the best for hop-growing. Thus it is that today you will only find oast houses, save for a few in Surrey, in these counties.

Sex rears its inquisitive head in the hop world as much as in any other. There are male and female hop plants. The male hop, when planted in the hop-garden, tends to increase the size of the cone of the female plant and the weight of the hop. The female flower, technically known as the strobile, is really the hop of commerce, and its functional parts are best seen in an early stage of growth when the hop is 'in burr'. The ovary, which contains a single ovule, is surmounted by two long stigmas with long hairs, or papillae.

The sex-life of the hop could fill a book of its own accord. However, the important point about hop-growing is its continuity, as the bines are perennial, throwing up new shoots every year. These bines climb up the strings which are set in position each spring by the men who, stepping from pole to pole on high stilts, conjure out of the hop-gardens a miracle of geometrically precise order, a pleasing pattern of poles and strings.

So much for the miracle wrought by man. It is he who in early spring coaxes the shoots up the strings by hand, a process known as 'twiddling'. But it is Nature which completes the miracle so that by late August the drowsily-scented bines, laden with golden hops, have climbed to the top of the strings and clothed the poles in a glory of gilded greenery.

'Hop-gardens,' writes Richard Church, 'are a sacred cult. Nobody who has not lived among them may know how deeply they enter into the life of the people. . . . The whole domestic economy centres round them. At three periods of the season, extending each over several weeks, the women have to leave their home duties for odd moments, so that they spend their working days in the gardens – first, with the stringing of the poles, second, with the twirling of the young bines when they begin to run, and, third, with the hop-picking at the crown of the year.'

In latter years there have been more women than men at work in the hop-gardens and this means that from late April until September many homes lose their most valued and trustworthy domestic servants. For it is a fact that the hop-garden worker is nearly always a respected and thoroughly reliable character, usually as skilled in the home as she is in the fields.

There is an echo of Dionysus in the hop-gardens and around the

oasts. You may see the latter in East Sussex sometimes singly, sometimes in pairs, quite often in clusters of hop kilns, comprising perhaps
dozens or a whole hamlet of oasts, lending to the English countryside
an aspect that is at once foreign and at once essentially native. They
remind me in many ways of the clusters of cupolas in the Souf towns
of Algeria; they are the English symbol of Bacchus, not of the grape
with its exotic bouquets of claret and Burgundy, but of the hop and its
multifarious blends of honest beer.

In southern France they tread the grape; in Sussex the precious hops
are dried in the round kilns which strangers often wrongly call oasts.
The oast is, in fact, the whole building, comprised of the receiving barn,
the drying floor and the kilns. But the aesthetic appeal lies in the oast
as a whole, its barn, its circular tower, or roundel, and the conical,
tapering, sharply sloping roof, surmounted by the cowl, a white-painted
dome with its long, slender arm turning majestically in the wind. It is
the slowly turning cowl and the swinging arm, often with a skilfully
carved weather-vane forming a superb silhouette against blue sky by
day and moonlight by night, which makes the oast as alive and romantic
as a ship in full sail:

> Red oast houses, fast climbing hops,
> Slanting their witches' hats against the sky.

A campaign to preserve oast houses has been undertaken by the
Rural Preservation Societies in Kent and East Sussex. There are several
hundred of these oasts in the two counties; some are still used for drying
hops, but the advent of mechanical processes for hop-drying has rendered
many of them obsolete. It is for this reason that these societies have
sought to save the dying and derelict oasts and to preserve the very best
specimens among them.

I delved fairly deeply into the history of oasts while considering
making one our home and I learned that the official view (and I am sure it
is the right one) is that the only worth-while oast is one which possesses
a cowl. 'The difference these make to the appearance of the oasts is
very great,' states the report of one Rural Preservation Committee,
'but once they have gone, the aesthetic appeal of the oast is seriously
diminished.'

This is perfectly true. Some oasts have had the cowls removed and
the flattened top of the roundel sealed up; they look poor, dead objects,
anachronisms without meaning. But an oast with its cowl, weaving into

the wind, is a thing of even greater beauty than a windmill. It is not the cheapest way of converting an oast into a home, for the maintenance costs are considerable. Every three years the cowl should be inspected and greased, and at least every five years taken down and painted, a major task for any building firm and one which any but a Kentish, or East Sussex builder may jib at. Nevertheless, it is well worth the effort for the sake of living in a place that exudes a purposeful activity from its fifty-foot pinnacle.

The oldest oast house I know is at Catt's Place, Paddock Wood, in the heart of the Whitbread country. It was built in the seventeenth century and has a link with the very early beginnings of the hop industry. As a single oast dries enough hops for some 11,000 barrels of beer in a single season, that at Catt's Place must in its time have processed enough hops for something like two and a half million barrels. Which is a thought-provoking example of statistology!

Once measured, the hops are packed into 'pokes' and taken to the oast houses, where they are spread on a hair mat which covers the latticed floor of the upper storey, there to be left to the assiduous care of the 'dryer', usually a highly skilled man with a long apprenticeship, who has acquired an uncanny knowledge of how to regulate the temperature of the glowing anthracite fires below. He adjusts the ventilating cowls through which percolates the sleepy scent of the drying flowers.

.   .   .   .   .

Once back in London, problems which in the mood of optimism induced by amber-hued cider at the Merry Damsel had seemed so easy of solution now appeared a hundred times magnified. Would the survey of the oast dampen my enthusiasm? Would the conversion of the building prove too costly? Could I convince the family that Codiham was a desirable village and that an oast would make a suitable home? This last task might have been much easier had I not telephoned late at night with such obvious delight in the 'wickedness' of Codiham. My wife suspected that I had been hopelessly misled by a villainous bunch of rustic pirates who saw a wonderful chance in palming off on me the most unsaleable property in the whole of Sussex.

'I'll give you my verdict when I see this precious discovery of yours,' was all she would say.

Which was fair enough. But I felt justified in reducing the risks of having my 'discovery' rejected by trying to create the right atmosphere for the family's first visit to Codiham. In this Mr. Pargetter proved an invaluable ally. I telephoned him and said:

'I wonder whether you could enter into a little plot to make sure that my family will really like Codiham. You see, an oast house as a dwelling will take some explanation. The idea has got to be put over carefully. . . .'

'I understand, sir.'

'Suppose I bring my family down to Codiham. Could you put us up?'

'Of course.'

'I mean rather more than that. How much would it cost to sleep in Miranda's Bed? You see, my wife has always had a thing about round beds. She – er – well, she rather favours the idea. And I thought it might make a romantic interlude if we slept in one, especially Miranda's. Quite mad, I know, but little novelties like this—'

'Can creat the right atmosphere?'

'Absolutely. Of course, I know this may be creating a precedent. And I should also like you to think up a special menu for dinner on the night we arrived.'

'You know, sir, this is the first request I have ever had from an Englishman to sleep in Miranda's Bed. My grandfather did tell me that King Edward VII slept there once at his own request. It may be true, but I fear my grandfather was rather a liar. A few years ago a French Ambassador slept in it. I could hardly refuse him. And I have had requests from Americans and quite a few film stars. I'm afraid I had to refuse them all, because the bed is a museum piece and a film star might give it all the wrong sort of publicity.'

'I should expect to pay extra for the privilege of sleeping in Miranda's Bed and I would promise to keep it secret.'

'I should love to help your wife and yourself, but—'

'Are there any other problems?'

'Well, sir, there is the problem of the sheets. It is a huge bed, and, being round into the bargain, the sheets would be difficult. I am trying to remember what happened when the French Ambassador came. I believe we had our laundress called in to stitch together several sheets. I'll find out if we still have the results of her sewing.'

'Then, you will—'

'There must be no question of establishing a precedent. On this understanding I'll do it. You say your son is interested in smugglers and secret passages. I think we had better book him into the Priest's Hole.'

'Oh, that would be splendid,' I added. 'It would make his day – I mean his night.'

Maybe you think I was taking unnecessary precautions to ensure that the rest of the family would like Codiham. You may, indeed, take the harsher view that I am a husband and father who needlessly feeds and encourages the wilder whims of wife and child. Perhaps. And yet there is also the other side to the question: the purely egotistical whim of the *paterfamilias* who enjoy these antics of detail, who savours the plaudits of a satisfied family.

Thus it was that, the problem of beds having been dealt with, Mr. Pargetter and I spent some minutes' earnest discussion of a menu for our dinner. I think we both enjoyed this, he, because at heart he loved people who took good food seriously, and I for the simple reason that a well-planned dinner is one of the most delightful mental exercises I know. And much more satisfying than doing a crossword puzzle.

The derelict oast at Codiham must have been about one hundred and thirty years old. Not the least of our troubles was that which the lawyers call the 'searches'. For one's title to the deeds of any property to be absolutely secure the 'searches' must be verified for a period of at least thirty years. During that time the oast had changed hands four times and the relevant papers were not easily obtainable.

The farm to which the oast originally belonged was one of the oldest in this part of the county – Half-Naker Farm, derived, no doubt, from the old English, *healfan-aecer*, meaning half a strip of ploughed land. The 'searches' revealed that the name of this farm was spelt in different ways in different documents. . . . Hafanaker, Ha'naker and, in the eighteenth century, Halfnaked, which somewhat ribald epithet had stuck and stayed. No wonder, for by the beginning of the century the farm was stripped almost naked; its fields were sold, its farm-houses pulled down to make way for new cottages and all that was left were three acres and an oast. By 1910 only the oast was left and in the late 'thirties the last hops were dried there.

In due course I had the surveyor's report. He completely de-romanticized the building in these terms:

'The drainage is stated to be the main sewer, but we cannot ascertain where the connexion to the sewer is made, as the drains pass on to the adjoining property beforehand. Nor do we quite see why or when they were made. However, your solicitors will no doubt make a point to ascertain that there are no difficulties as to this. The general structure appears to be quite sound and could be converted into a dwelling. Some of the tiling on the oast requires attention; re-tiling will be a problem because of the necessity for obtaining a tile that is not too heavy.

The cowl functions, but is slightly out of alignment and requires greasing and overhauling, also painting. You may decide to have this removed and the top of the oast sealed off; on the other hand by retaining the cowl you will get ample ventilation. You should watch for trouble from smoking chimneys, when they are built, due to the very tall oast roof which would inevitably tower over the stacks; a revolving chimney cowl would seem to be the answer.'

Needless to add I did not let my wife get a glimpse of the surveyor's report at this early stage in the negotiations. That might well have been fatal. But I sweated and chilled alternately in the meantime at the thought of how deeply I was committed. True, I had paid the deposit, but that was returnable. On the other hand, as the survey seemed, with reservations, to give me the signal to go ahead, I had to make a decision fairly soon. Yet suppose Sylvia failed to like Codiham? Would she take an instant dislike to 'Sailor' Thompsett? Would the famous King's Damsel's Bed be regarded as a joke in bad taste? You can, perhaps, see how and why I planned so desperately and at the same time deliberately to make the trip to Codiham an unqualified success.

After all, when one considered that we had, during our Grand Tour of villages, rejected almost contemptuously some of the most renowned in England, that we had looked down our noses at picturesque cottages smothered in honeysuckle, it was difficult for Sylvia to accept on my word alone the peculiar magic of a place called 'Codgem', not to mention the idea of living in a hop-drying room.

4. *Ivory tower in an oast house*

ONE Wednesday afternoon we took a fast train to Wadhurst and travelled on to Codiham by taxi. Wadhurst wasn't the nearest station and the taxi-drive added what may have seemed an unnecessary thirty-five shillings to the travelling fares. But I had worked out that the drive was part of the build-up for the arrival in Codiham, especially as it lay through some of the loveliest parts of the Weald and obviated any changing of trains. Codiham Station, I might add, which was a mile from the village anyhow, had been closed down as 'uneconomical' by our parsimonious nationalized railway authority two years before.

'So there is no station in your precious village?' inquired my wife. 'How does one travel to and from it in the ordinary way, by horse?'

I chortled nervously. 'Well, darling, we want to escape from noise.'

'We could, of course, do that by emigrating to the North Pole,' she commented acidly.

I refrained from pointing out that the original idea of hunting for a new home had been hers.

Luck was against me. It happened to be one of those days when it was not only raining, but seemed unlikely to cease raining; at Wadhurst rain gave place to a deluge of hailstones. Sylvia looked pretty fed up and I cast about me for some gambit with which to enliven the conversation.

'You realize, darling, that you are about to see what you have always wanted to possess?'

'What's that?'

'Why, a round bed. The famous King's Damsel's Bed. It's quite fabulous.'

'Well, I'm not going to Codiham to buy it. I don't see the association of ideas at all.'

'Er – no, darling, but you have more than once expressed a desire for a round bed.'

'I think such a bed would look much more attractive than an oblong bed. No horrid, ugly corners. But just what are you up to? Why this sudden concern for my taste in beds?'

It was no good. I was still under suspicion; every word I uttered could be construed as part of some subtle plot for getting my own way. We sat back in silence until we approached Codiham.

As the taxi drew up at the Merry Damsel Young George appeared holding a large umbrella. He looked like a racecourse tout offering odds and was grinning hugely, which made me more apprehensive. Still, thanks to Young George, we made the hotel without getting soaked and blinded by hailstones.

'Good afternoon, sir, good afternoon, madam. And is this the young gentleman who's going to sleep in our smugglers' hide-out?'

'Smugglers' hide-out?' inquired young Anthony excitedly. 'Have you really got one? You didn't tell me, Daddy,' he added reproachfully.

'It was to be a surprise,' I explained.

'Oh, yes,' said Young George, 'us be proper wicked down at Codgem—'

'So I have heard,' politely but ironically added Sylvia.

'Yes,' said Young George, not noticing this subtle barb, 'our smugglers was a wicked old lot. This room you're agoin' to sleep in was a Priest's Hole once upon a time. That's what we still call it. After that it were used by smugglers. You'll see Bristol Glass rolling-pins hanging on the walls; they was used by the smugglers to 'ide their rum and brandy in.'

Delightedly my son clapped his hands and went off gaily to inspect the Priest's Hole and to listen to Young George's stories about priests being smuggled over to France and kegs of brandy being stowed under 'the very bed in which you'll sleep tonight'. I then knew I had one ally in the battle for who was to live in Codiham.

Silently we went up to Miranda's Room. It was on the first floor, overlooking the rose garden and the tiny courtyard with the fig-tree growing in it. As the door was opened the King's Damsel's Bed appeared in all its gilded splendour. As I have already quoted from the magazine description of this bed, I will not add any further technical details beyond adding that it looked like something specially built for a scene from a French farce. It was more like a tent than a bed, with its striped curtains in red and white, billowing round the bronze posts on which the golden cupids were pursuing undressed maidens with their arrows.

'You don't mean to say that you have been so mad as to book this bed for us to sleep in?' demanded Sylvia.

'But, darling, you adore round beds. You know you do.'

'Surely this is a museum piece. No one could possibly sleep in it. How does one arrange the sheets?'

'Well, they seem to be arranged all right now. After all, there is plenty of room. It's twelve feet in diameter.'

'Oh, there's plenty of room, madam,' said Young George. 'In fact, way back early in the last century a party of what they called Regency bucks spent the night in it – all eight of 'em. A rare old party they 'ad afore they turned in.'

'Oh, well,' replied Sylvia, 'I'll try anything once. But I doubt if I'll retain my affection for round beds after seeing this monstrosity. I shudder to think that I shall be ogled by cupids all night.'

'I hope it ull be all right, sir,' said Young George in a whisper as I left the room. 'I allus did think you was taking a risk in booking this room. Reckon as my missus'ud kick up a shindy if I put *her* in that bed.'

Round about opening time the climate improved. Not only the weather, but the domestic climate when Sylvia had unpacked, sipped one of Mr. Pargetter's dry martinis and then asked for another.

'I've not had a martini like this in ages,' she purred blissfully.

'I don't always make them like that, madam,' explained the landlord. 'The trouble is that few people are agreed on what a good dry martini should be. Seventy per cent of those who ask for them have never tasted a good martini. They only want half and half. Then there are about ten per cent who don't seem to mind how weak the martini is as long as there is a large lump of ice floating in it. But the whole secret of a good dry martini is plenty of gin and no lumps of ice to dilute it. Always mistrust anyone who hands you a dry martini within two minutes of asking for it. It can't be done. A really good dry martini is really an English drink based entirely on a first-class, dry English gin. You put a dash of vermouth in a shaker, swill it round and pour it away except for a tiny drop at the bottom. Then you pour in your gin, shake it around, pour the whole into a glass and pop the glass into the refrigerator. Leave it there for three minutes, then serve it with lemon peel. Peel, I might say, and not in any circumstances any of the fruit or juice of the lemon. The result is ninety-eight per cent gin and two per cent vermouth.'

The sun had unexpectedly come out and we walked round the Green to view the oast house. By night it looked rather like an illustration for Poe's *The Fall of the House of Usher*; by day it was just a picturesque ruin. On one side, separated by a clump of firs, was the church; fortunately the firs hid the graveyard. On the other side was what 'Sailor' Thompsett had described as 'Mad Miranda's House'. Apparently the daughter of the landlord of the Merry Damsel had done fairly well for herself out of her liaison with Charles II. Though undoubtedly a mere passing interlude in that monarch's tempestuous love life, she had acquired sufficient funds to build a black-and-white gabled house where she installed herself with some lavishness. More attractive than the house were the wrought-iron gates. These were fixed to massive stone pillars on each of which was carved the head of a woman with the body of a bitch. Local legend had it that this was Miranda's revenge on Charles's two most notorious mistresses, the Duchesses of Cleveland and Portsmouth; certainly the heads resembled portraits of this pair.

But the best feature of the oast was that it looked out across Cucking Green and just over the road was the pond where Codiham's erring wives had been ducked in bygone days. About an acre in size, it made a perfect home for two swans and a cygnet. At one time there had been as many as ten members of the swan family on the pond. Then, in 1952, a pen died and four of her young only lived another eight days before they were eaten by rats. A year later the cob of the pair then on the pond was killed by a boy with a catapult. Accordingly, the pen reigned alone and when a cob was taken to woo her, she chivied him off the water. But Codiham regarded its swans as Gibraltar regards her Rock Apes, and a parish council meeting decided that replacements must be found.

Sylvia was so delighted with the swans she almost forgot about the oast. But my son, Anthony, was already inspecting the ruin and planning how the half-acre of land should be utilized, pacing out a potential cricket pitch. Meanwhile, I had arranged to meet a local builder at the oast and was fully occupied in listening to his suggestions.

'Mistake most people make when they convert an oast is to try to be too clever with the roundel,' was his first comment. 'Now the great thing is not to waste space. You've got a whole heap of room in this roundel, and you should never disremember that.'

D

I was learning my Sussex gradually; 'disremember', however, was a new one and reminiscent of Huckleberry Finn.

'You've got the space for a fine round room on the ground floor, twenty feet in diameter. Now above that you can get a bedroom which won't be quite round, but the biggest part of a circle. You must leave a tiny space for stairs and passage. So there you'll have a straight line of a wall to put the backs of your beds to, and a long round wall facing you. You can get three windows in that round wall and have plenty of light.

'Above that again there's space for another room. In fact, you could get two more rooms, with one above the other, but I'd advise you to settle for only three rooms in the roundel each above t'other.'

Sylvia's main immediate interest was the question of heating. 'Yes, doubtless, the walls are very thick. But wouldn't an oast be awfully cold? After all, it isn't built for living in.'

'You can have a large brick fireplace in the ground oast room, madam,' replied the builder. 'That'll be no problem once we've fixed a proper chimney and cowl. A lobster pot cowl, I'd suggest. But if you start having that central heating, you'll be putting your bill up and no mistake, and simply eating up your space. And you mustn't waste space.'

Wasting space was, one gathered, the besetting sin in the opinion of Dick Pride, the builder. He was an honest craftsman, as much anxious to make a decent job of conversion as to make a fair profit. And he had that rare quality among builders, a horror of extravagance. But on one point he was quite adamant that we should have to be prepared to spend a lot of money.

'What about the roof?' asked Sylvia. 'Some of those tiles look unsafe to me. Do they leak?'

Dick Pride scratched his head in a worried manner. 'Now spending money is summat I dursn't like any more'n you. But in my opinion you'd be very unwise to leave that roof as it is, or just to patch it up. I'd suggest scrapping the tiles and replacing 'em with cedar shingles.'

'Whew!' I said. 'That's going to cost a packet. Is it essential?'

'You'll have *boco*[1] trouble with the roof, if you don't. And or'nary tiles ud be too heavy. Cedar shingles are light and make a first-class job.'

'What about the risk of fire?'

---

[1] *Boco* is East Sussex dialect for 'plenty'. It obviously derives from the French and was probably introduced by Huguenot immigrants.

'Not a chance. The roof's too steep for anything to lay on and catch alight. And the cedar shingles wouldn't be over wood. No, there's no risk of fire.'

We talked and talked, argued and probed, and still Sylvia hadn't given a decision. The builder promised to see us again in the morning. We went back to the Merry Damsel for two more martinis and then had dinner. Mr. Pargetter had excelled himself. There was, to start with, Mermaid's Pie, a long-forgotten Sussex coastal recipe which the industrious landlord must have resurrected from that treasure-house of a cellar. It consisted of flaky pastry covering a mixture of scollops, shrimps, crayfish, chives, mushrooms and anchovies, a piscatorial feast in itself. This was followed by roast duck and pineapple sauce, with fresh green peas from the garden, pancakes flaming in kirsch and a huge home-made cheese.

The hour of decision was at hand. It arrived with the coffee and the Merry Damsel's home-brewed cherry brandy. Seizing my one and only cheroot, which I had carefully laid beside me, Sylvia placed it in her mouth and lit it.

'We'll buy it,' was all she said, and I was completely taken off balance. 'I cannot bear to see you writhing uneasily any longer. The thought of your hovering round that enormous bed waiting for me to say "yes" to Codiham is more than I can bear. You can now resume behaving with your normal, characteristic casualness. I don't think I can stand another moment of these unexpected attentions. For the first time since our honeymoon you actually remembered that kirsch is my favourite liqueur.'

'What about that cigar?' I asked, more to hide my secret delight than anything else. 'I can, of course, get another, but do you think it's quite the thing to do down at Codiham?'

' "Us be proper wicked down at Codgem",' was the smiling reply.

To which there was no answer. And so the battle – if ever there had really been any battle except in my imagination – was won. Obviously, the delayed decision was my punishment for staying out all night a week previously.

. . . . .

Vatsayana, in defining the 'sixty-four accessory arts for women', specifically mentions 'making different kinds of beds for different seasons and for different purposes'. I don't know whether Vatsayana had in mind a bed anything like that in which Miranda dallied with Charles II, but he might well have done. As soon as we climbed into this vast ocean of linen I knew that it was a mistake and thanked heaven that the decision to buy the oast had been confirmed. The frolicsome cupids were a constant irritation; their indecent antics prevented all thoughts of sleep and we both longed to tear down the striped curtains which made us feel as though we were two lone artists under a huge circus tent.

It had been an eventful day and sleep defied us. Ultimately I decided to creep downstairs and purchase from Young George half a bottle of the Merry Damsel's cherry brandy. This we drank in our half-Byzantine, half-Restoration museum piece as we discussed the methods which the Merry Monarch must have used to lure the innkeeper's daughter into this veritable rostrum of a bed. It was not a comfortable night; my weight seemed to throw the whole bed out of balance and it was obvious that the mattress (not the one, I might add, on which Charles and Miranda slept) and the base of the bed did not coincide in a strictly Euclidian sense. In the morning when we awoke from a much-disturbed slumber we were both agreed we could not recommend the bed to any bridal pair.

'I shouldn't wish my biggest enemy of the female sex to spend her bridal night in this bed,' was Sylvia's terse comment.

But there was little time in which to ponder on beds. We had another long session with the builder, during which it was agreed that we would have the roof of the oast tiled with cedar shingles. The cowl we unanimously decided to retain and Dick Pride suggested that 'as we've got to take un down, we might as well make it more purty like'. His idea of something 'purty' was to carve out some kind of an emblem on the end of the cowl arm. He suggested 'a sarpint, they being very popular on oasts in these parts'. Anthony wanted a skull and crossbones; I favoured the Sussex martlets, but the builder wisely pointed out that this 'ud look anything but what it's supposed to be from a distance'.

Sylvia, illogical as women usually are, wanted a white horse. 'But this is Sussex, not Kent,' indignantly interjected Dick Pride. 'A white horse is a Kentish emblem.'

'Well, anyhow, I think a white horse would look much better than your silly martlets – who knows what a martlet is, any way? – and less sinister than a serpent. A white horse would look very attractive against the skyline.'

Aesthetically she was doubtless right. So we compromised by making it a winged horse design of Pegasus and I had to confess that the deflater of Bellerophon's bombast made an admirable motif for our swinging cowl.

Instructions were given as to how the new home was to take shape and all that now remained was for the respective lawyers to write letters to each other and argue incessantly about the 'searches' and lost deeds. At times we doubted whether we should ever really be able to call that oast our own. When it was not the 'searches' holding us up, it was some problem about the Local Authority and the drains, or right of access, or town planning. There must have been a score or more of these letters to and fro before one day the contracts were signed. Ah, now, I thought, it's in the bag. But no, the only real security would come with the conveyancing, and there was a last-minute hitch on that.

Codiham was very jealous of its 'rural amenities' and as this was the only oast house in the main street of the village and facing the Green, the local authorities insisted that the conversion should be in accordance with their views of what was right and proper. They need not have worried; our main concern was for the completed home still to look as much of an oast house as ever.

To buy a house in England today is rarely easy, even if you have the cash, which few of us can claim is other than borrowed. But, should you be rash enough to think of buying an oast house, the frustrations and exasperations are manifold. But from such frustrations one learns much. If you are the owner of a really old property and it has been approved by an insurance company, my experience is that you can be far more certain of your entitlement to the deeds than by any other method of purchase. Far too many old houses are sold with none too meticulous solicitors merely satisfying themselves that 'searches' dating back fifteen years are sufficient. They are nothing of the sort and it is most unwise to accept any such opinion. Access to the roof of any old building is also all-important. If any such access is boarded up, suspect it at once: it may hide dry-rot in the beams, or woodworm. Equally one should watch out for any floors which may be covered with hard-board, a modern trick with the spiv conversionist and one which he is too often allowed to get away with by casual surveyors. A personal survey, apart from that of the building society or insurance company, is essential. That may sound extremely odd, but it happens to be true.

I make these rather dreary observations in the hope that they may save similar town-bumpkins like ourselves from starting off on the wrong foot in quest of the Perfect Life in the country. It is also as well to remember that the country is colder than the town and that heating is almost next to godliness. Certainly lack of it can turn a charitable Christian into a bad-tempered pagan.

The day came when all was signed and sealed and the oast was ours. Doubtless we made errors and are still discovering them. We should have had central heating, but three arguments hardened us against this. In the first place, whenever I think of oil heating I picture the gangster moguls of that commodity who, whether in the Middle East or Texas, can hold this tiny island to ransom on the question of oil supplies. Secondly, we have a ridiculous prejudice against this modern invention and its hideous pipes and soulless apparatus. But ultimately our decision was clinched because we had decided to spend the extra money on cedar shingles. And if it were a case of choosing between cedar shingles for the roof, or central heating again, I think I should still make the same choice. Nevertheless, we soon found we had to conserve every therm we could, to insulate the roof and prevent a mass migration of warm air into the top of the oast.

One of the attractions of an oast-house home is its spaciousness and freedom from a forest of beams on which to bang your head. Our beams were snug against the ceilings and we left them just as they were. Another consideration is that a round room is light and airy; you can have at least two windows, sometimes three.

Once she had decided to accept the oast as our future residence my wife, like a field marshal in the War Office, took control of the situation with the light of battle in her eye. Decisions sprang like crackerjacks from the fertile imagination which she brought to bear on dull plaster walls and bare windows. This was her sphere and she knew exactly what was required. Do not misunderstand me when I use this martial simile. It is not meant unkindly. But when I saw her pouring over patterns of curtain and carpet materials like a campaigner reading maps, or crisply telephoning a dozen stores until she found what she wanted, I realized that a bloodless revolution was taking place under my nose. Red brocade curtains with fancifully carved pelmets were to mask the gaping spaces in the walls and undreamed of combinations of colour to transform the utilitarian walls of the oast.

The main room – call it lounge, drawing-room, or what you will, but we decided simply to name it the oast room – was obviously the place for a party. There was the big brick fireplace on one side and the heat from this seemed to throw itself equally to all walls; one just put chairs and settees in a circle round the walls, with a wide-open space in the middle. At least this was how we experimented one winter's day when we went back to Codiham to plan the more intimate details of living. In such a room no one could be tucked away in a corner, for there weren't any corners; what better setting for a convivial evening. The habit of sitting away from the fireplace came naturally; there was none of that shutting away of the rest of the room by crowding around the burning logs.

One snag was fitted carpets. It is about the only thing to do with round rooms. Expensive, but snugger than rugs and certainly easier to clean. Or so I am told. But the wastage of carpet is appalling as the piles of bits and pieces in the box-room now reveal.

We had made an ivory tower of our oast home and, having been obliged to compromise on many things (being in effect the field marshal's orderly!), I stuck out boldly for an ivory tower of my own at the top of the oast. Here, under the swinging cowl, with a view of the swans on the pond and, at night, Miranda's portrait flood-lit at the other end of Cucking Green, I created a study. It was in that part of the roundel where, half-way up the wall the conical roof began, so it was a queer-shaped room with walls that tapered inwards. I found that the view was so enchantingly distracting that I had to push my desk away from it to avoid all the temptations to wander down to the Merry Damsel, or to have a beer with 'Sailor' Thompsett at the Bearpits.

But all this took shape slowly. It would be pointless to enumerate all our teething troubles, the prolonged tiling of the roof, the experiments with different types of chimney cowls before we solved the problem of skirling, clerical-grey fumes driven down the chimneys. The oast cowl was brought down to the ground, painted white and the model of Pegasus duly attached before it was once again hoisted skywards to perform its eternal task of following the wind.

Outside, the roundel was given a pale lemon wash. From the rotting timber in the wilderness around the oast Dick Pride salvaged three huge old beams out of which he created a massive front door. It was the sort of door which cried out for an equally massive knocker and a brass lion from an antique shop in Tunbridge Wells supplied the answer. There remained the question of squeezing a dining-room into an awkward L-shaped space between the front door and the staircase. If we had a separate dining-room, it would be so cramped as to be ridiculous and unworthy of the name; if we used the L-shape as a dining-hall, there was the threat of draughts. But this, we decided, could wait until we were in.

Electricity was laid on, the drains were pronounced in order, water gurgled through the pipes and all was ready for the exodus from Ealing. It now remained to be seen how Codiham would take the invasion of its cherished Green by a trio of innocent townsfolk.

5. *Of bear-baiting, smuggling, cucking and kissing*

A VILLAGE without a history is a poor, meaningless, sorry sort of place, set in the countryside, but not of it, either aggressively self-assertive, or shamefacedly apologetic. It is a place apart from nature, lacking any *élan vital*.

History, it might well be said, is man's last line of defence, his one excuse for trying to do anything at all. It has always angered me that history is invariably regarded at our universities as one of those subjects in which it is easiest to obtain a degree. Probably that is why we are cursed more than any other nation with such soulless historians. It is fashionable to sneer at Sir Winston Churchill's *History of the English-Speaking Peoples*, to damn it as romantic and dealing in battles instead of industrial revolutions. I wonder what made us so quixotically anxious to defend our island in 1940 – a recollection of the Chartists, or the Manchester School of Liberals, or the nursery tales of Alfred and the burnt cakes, or Nelson putting his blind eye to the telescope?

It is in spite of the professional historians with their donnish, statistics-minded, jaundiced pens that we remain a great nation. They, more than anyone else today, have sought to denigrate our achievements, to obliterate our traditions in a welter of theories. It has always been the amateur, with a sense of spirit and individualism, an eye for colour and the trivial pastimes of past generations of men and women, who has gleaned and harvested for us a history which is also a way of life. Kipling, with all his faults, was a better historian of the British Raj than the modern apologists.

It would be a platitude to say that Codiham owed everything to its history. Yet, without that history, would Codiham have defied the centuries, retaining its individualism with a robust, rearguard action against the encroachment of bureaucracy on the one hand and standard-ization on the other? I rather doubt it. Indeed, I will go further than this; I assert emphatically that Codiham owes much to its traditional 'wickedness' and native cunning.

Codiham means simply the place, or home of Coda. The origins of the village are obscure, but it seems fairly certain that Coda was a Saxon chieftain who built a small settlement in the Weald. His coming must have followed the attack by Cissa and Ella on the British in the great forest of Anderida, which resulted in the founding of the South-Saxon kingdom. The Andreasweald Forest must have surrounded Codiham in those days and this may be why it was never exploited by the Romans; certainly there are no traces of Roman work in the immediate vicinity.

Probably the village was attacked by the Danes, for in 1826 the wreck of a Danish vessel was found ten feet beneath the mud of the River Dentical. In those days the river was navigable for fair-sized ships and the now disused quay behind the Hole in the Wall received shipping as long ago as the early part of the eleventh century. But the oldest remaining building in the vicinity of the village is the ruin of Westhurst Abbey which stands at the edge of Ghost's Wood, a melancholic, decayed fragment of three walls and some rather exquisite arches. There used to be a local superstition in Codiham that if a lad and a lass watched the harvest moon rise through the large window at the end of the ruined nave, they would be married within the year and live happily ever after. I am afraid that the advent of television has long since discouraged such romantic pilgrimages.

Westhurst Abbey dates back to A.D. 719, when the manor of *West-hurstia juxta Codium* was granted to the Abbot. For more than two hundred years the Church enjoyed its manor, green and pond; then the Normans swiftly took possession of all materially desirable things in the area. Domesday Book relates that '*Idem Gislebertus tenet Westhurstia cum Manerio Regis de Codgem*'. Filbert apparently was the Norman usurper, and in 1085 Codgem (as it was then so spelt) was accounted worth '£8 and 6d.' and had '8 villains, 8 bodarii, 2 serfs, a mill of 50d., a fishery of 40d., 12 acres of pasture, wood for 20 pigs and land for 7 ploughs'.

The Church of Saint Mildred – an uncommon dedication – was first built in 1094, but few traces of its Norman origin now remain. The tower and steeple were erected in the fourteenth century and wealthy local traders insisted that 'nothing but Bethersden marble will suffice to pay our tribute to God'. Unhappily much of the early history of the church and indeed of Codiham itself has been lost through some prisoners in the former village jail breaking out and destroying the local archives in the sixteenth century.

The church tower is 120 feet high and on a clear day you can see a long distance across the English Channel from its summit. An old Codiham saying runs:

> If from the tower you can see France,
> Gather hay while there's the chance;
> If clouds and mist do hide the sea,
> Surelye there'll be rain ere tea.

Personally, I have never yet seen the coast of France from Codiham Church tower, though 'Sailor' Thompsett swears that 'as a kid I used to see it most summers, afore this cursed hydra-headed bomb was invented'.

According to local tradition a beacon was lit from the church tower at the time of the Spanish Armada, but the importance of the village was beginning to diminish in Elizabethan times and, when Queen Elizabeth I visited Sussex, she deliberately avoided Codiham as a mark of her disapproval of its squire.

Saint Mildred's owes what beauty she possesses almost entirely to her spire and tower. The main building is by no means beautiful, but the nave roof is the only one in England, save one, to be covered with oak shingles – a most unusual material – while the barrel-vault ceiling inside is of the fifteenth century and superbly carved.

The bells of long ago were made by quite a small number of bell-founders with the result that you often find bells cast in Codiham in such distant counties as Norfolk and Suffolk. In the fourteenth century the village could boast of a bell-foundry and *The Book of the Names and Ordinancies of the Cutlers' and Bell-founders' Company* lists Simon Ferrier as the chief of local bell-founders. It is recorded that he had three attempts at making the tenor bell for Saint Mildred's and another ancient rhyme goes:

Three times run and three times cast,
Codiham's tenor cast at last!

The belfry at the parish church is well worth a visit. It contains eight bells, the total weight of which is more than four tons. The inscriptions on them are worthy of note, but they must have been added when the bells were recast in 1760:

1st bell: If you have a musical ear, you'll admit I'm sweet and clear;

2nd bell: Ring me and the welkin rings, hope eternal from me springs;

3rd bell: For Saint Mildred I will toll, for the mercy of her soul;

4th bell: In this bell you'll take delight to make it go with all its might;

5th bell: All ye who listen to me ring, stand ye fast for God and King;

6th bell: In wedlock ye who do unite my tuneful tongue sounds nuptial rite;

7th bell: Double Norwich Court Bob Majors, Stedman Caters, Grandsire Trebles; all these you'll ring with many changes, as Man proposes and God arranges;

8th bell: Last am I, but not the least, to offer you a heavenly feast.

The Reverend Martyn Bowker, vicar of Codiham, has made a lifelong hobby of campanology and to him we owe a fascinating history of Codiham's bells and bell-foundry. Alas, the bell-foundry is no longer there, much to the vicar's regret. But he has done his best to revive the ancient traditions of bell-ringing and got together as good a team as can be found for many miles around. When he came to the church he discovered that the oak hangings of the bells had been badly damaged by woodworm. By dint of sheer hard work and enthusiasm he managed to raise the £400 required to repair the damage.

'It was hard work for a foreigner like myself to make the villagers bell-minded,' Mr. Bowker told me. 'Then, one Sunday, when we were without bell-ringers, I decided to ring the bells myself – or, at least, some of them. I thought a familiar tune might do the trick, so I chimed out "Three Blind Mice". You should have seen the congregation attracted out of sheer curiosity. After that the idea of playing tunes on the bells appealed strongly to the junior members of the Church. It reached its climax when our junior ringers – all boys and girls from the village – tried out the "Harry Lime Theme" on Guy Fawkes night. I'm afraid that didn't go down at all well with the old folks.'

Mr. Bowker discovered on the second bell an inscription which had been partly erased to make room for the sentiment expressed in 1760. This stated quite simply 'NIL DESPERANDUM'. Could this have been the tenor bell which gave so much trouble in casting? The art of deciphering bells is one in which Mr. Bowker is particularly well versed. Most bells are stamped with the founder's mark and often with his name, initials or crest. He has discovered that Simon Ferrier used the initials S. F. and an anvil for a crest, which seems to suggest that Simon was also the local blacksmith.

Furnaces flourished in Codiham in the days before coal from the north ousted Sussex iron and left the land free for hop-poles and agriculture. Some of the hop-gardens today mask old hammer ponds and in 1653 'Codgem' is mentioned as 'mayking guns and cannon for war'. The mulberry trees still standing in the garden of the Bearpits' public house are the sole remaining trace of what was once Codiham's silk industry. The adjacent street is still named Mulberry Street and off it leads Silk Lane. In Tudor times the village must have been extremely prosperous, probably rivalling many large towns in the wealth it produced.

But a decline in the fortunes of the village set in early in Elizabeth I's reign. It was about this time that Codiham earned its reputation for 'wickedness'. The chief culprit was Sir Jervis Thyme, a ruffian sea captain who built Cucking Manor on the opposite side of the Green to Mad Miranda's house. Sir Jervis had gravely offended the Queen; it was probably fortunate for him that she never visited Codiham. The manor was undoubtedly built from the proceeds of his piracy on the high seas; the knighthood he did not achieve until James I came to the throne.

The Church of Saint Mildred contains his tomb with a rather frightening mail-clad effigy of this giant of a man. Of course the living was in his name, otherwise it is exceeding doubtful whether so diabolical a character would have found such a resting-place. He had four wives and twelve children. The first wife was found at the bottom of a well, believed to have been hurled down it by her husband, though no one could prove this. The second disappeared and was never found; the third and fourth died in childbirth and it was after this that Sir Jervis suddenly developed a taste for human flesh. Some said he acquired this bestial taste on his travels to the West Indies; whatever the reasons for his passion the fact was that on certain nights villagers passing Cucking Manor swore they sniffed the smoke of burning human flesh pouring from the chimneys.

In his lifetime nothing was ever proved against Sir Jervis, but children from Codiham and other villages were constantly disapppearing and it was rumoured that he paid a high price for some unwanted, new-born child. In appearance he became more and more bloated and dissipated and stranger in his behaviour. After his death his son ordered the garden of Cucking Manor to be dug up; sure enough, several feet down were found the bones and skeletons of babies: not a particle of flesh was left.

This news must have caused a tremendous sensation in the neighbour-hood and, gossip being what it is, always the better for embellishment, a Sussex legend was created. The Codgem Cannibals – that was how the people of near-by towns and villages contemptuously referred to the unfairly maligned inhabitants of Codiham. The epithet lasted until the 'seventies of the last century, for in 1872 there was formed a football team calling themselves the Codiham Cannibals: as Young George always says, 'We've got a proper sense of 'umour down at Codgem.'

But if the reputation for wickedness was undeserved in the beginning, there can be no denying that Codiham soon learned to live up to its tradition – not perhaps as cannibals, but certainly as murderers, thieves, bear-baiters, fornicaters, cock-fighters and smugglers. Each century until the end of the eighteenth seemed to change the village's inhabitants for the worse. And the squires of Codiham, though never exceeding Sir Jervis in wickedness, by no means set their tenants a good example.

It is said that since the death of Sir Jervis, who, incidentally, died of an attack of indigestion, no Thyme has ever since died in bed except for the fourteenth baronet who spoilt the record by dying in a Parisian brothel in 1873. When the family solicitor returned home with such displeasing tidings, the painting of Hector Thyme was turned to the wall and so, by family custom, it remains to this day, a conspicuous rebuke not so much to his profligacy, as to the fact that he is the only Thyme since Sir Jervis not to have died with his boots on.

Sir Nathaniel Thyme (1633–87) was a *flaneur* and wit at the Court of Charles II. Either in the year 1668 or 1669 Charles II paid a visit to Codiham and stayed at Cucking Manor, for in the old churchwardens' accounts for those years there is the following item: 'Spent upon the Ringers when his Majesty was at Codiham, 11s. 8d.'

During that visit the King called at the Merry Damsel, where his ever wayward eye was directed upon Miranda, the maiden daughter of the inn-keeper, Isaac Puttock. He is said to have observed that she was indeed 'a Merry Damsel and the inn is well named'. He brought with him the Earl of Rochester and that rakish poet wrote of Miranda:

When wearied with a life at Court,
To gay Miranda I return,
To liquid lips and bosoms taut;
For honeyed kisses I do yearn.

But it was Charles, not Rochester, who gained the 'liquid lips' and 'honeyed kisses'. Not so easily as all that, however. Miranda played 'hard to get'; she demanded that if the King wished to spend the night with her, he must provide a bed worthy of a 'Scilly Sussex Maid'. Incidentally, it is a fallacy to refer to Sussex people as 'Silly Sussex'; the origin of the phrase is 'Scilly[1] Sussex', which means 'Holy Sussex'. And Miranda, a hypocritical little puss, pretended to be more virtuous than in reality she was.

The Merry Monarch bargained equally hardly. If he returned to Codiham, he must be received with due honour by the villagers and he let it be known that he would expect a silver loving cup, suitably inscribed, to be presented to him. 'Codgem', as shrewd and wicked as ever, knew quite well that Charles's sole purpose in visiting their village again was for seduction, and the villagers decided that the King himself should pay for this presentation. This they contrived in an ingenious manner; each villager was instructed to clip small pieces from any silver coins he might possess and the clippings were fashioned into a cup.

Charles kept his word about the bed. It was duly delivered – not to Miranda, or it probably wouldn't be in the Merry Damsel today – but to her father. Charles is said to have told Miranda that he had provided 'a bed big enough for a stallion to rest in'. That he slept in it we must accept, for a tablet on the base of one of the bronze columns records the fact. As, however, this tablet was inscribed in Victorian times, doubtless the prudery of the period demanded that there should be no mention of Miranda having shared it with him. Mrs. Aphra Behn, that bawd of Restoration writers, seems to have had no doubts at all about this.

Miranda eventually became quite wealthy and the home she built on the Green was the scene of many masques and balls. She shocked the villagers with her unconventional behaviour and her blackamoor servants who dressed like Turks. Later, it is said, she became the mistress of Sir Nathaniel Thyme and that her house was little better than a place of assignation. But she remained unmarried and in her declining years made amends by reviving her reputation of being a 'Scilly Sussex Maid', donating a font to the church. Even in this instance she could not resist

[1] A corruption of the Saxon *Selig* = Holy.

having a joke, for the angel on the font was carved in her likeness as a girl. There can't be many churches which possess a whore's head on their fonts! Mr. Bowker, who is not without a worldly sense of humour, says that what with the font and Sir Jervis's tomb, Saint Mildred bears all the burden of Codiham's wickedness.

Phillip Stubbes was scathing about Codiham's morals.

'Cucking Green,' he wrote, 'is no better than the stewes of London . . . every saucy boy of fourteen, sixteen or twenty years is intent to have his prettie pussie to huggle withall. Round the maypole what smouching and slabbering one of another, what filthy groping and unclean handling is practised in these dancings, what clipping and culling, what kissing and bussing, and above all the bawdy practice of cucking which so brings the parish into disrepute.'

'Cucking' is the name which the villagers have for centuries given to a peculiar local amatory recreation. Whether 'cucking' took its name from the Green, or the Green from 'cucking' I cannot say. Nobody seems to be sure. But 'cucking', according to Stubbes's own definition, seems to be the

'bestial practice by which boys and girls do take each other into the rotting, hollowed-out refuges in the trees of the Green, there to make tryst and conduct most unseemly rites. The girl first removes her garter, which is treated as though it were a saint's relic; this is handed to the boy who attaches it to the tree as a sign of his right to the place for future manifestations of the filthy, diabolical habit of cucking.

He must then give to the maid his perfumed glove which she will request him to place in her bosom. They will then write their names on the tree, linking them in the shape of a heart, and are tiresomely addicted to pretty diminutives in their conversation, like bird, mouse, lamb, puss, pigeon, pigsney, kid, honey, love, dove, cockalorum and chicken.'

'Cucking' still goes on of a night on the Green and is even regarded by some villagers as a Sussex version of bundling. I myself can find little present-day parallel with bundling, but Young George says his grandmother used to be taken by her father to an old oak on the Green, where she was tied and trussed up to her 'young man'. There they remained 'innercent-like, save for a bit of bussing and cuddling, until great-grandpapa came along to let 'em loose at nine o'clock prompt. Then he took his daughter home.'

We shall hear more about 'cucking' later on, for shortly after I arrived in Codiham it became a major issue in the discussions of the Parish Council.

If the Puritans condemned Codiham for 'kissing, bussing and cucking', their descendants of the eighteenth century had no qualms about indulging in smuggling. As Nonconformists they regarded smuggling as an honourable profession. Two hundred years ago the sea came within six miles of Codiham; today it is three miles farther off. Then the River Dentical was not so silted up as it is now and cargoes of lace, brandy, rum and tea were brought on dark nights to the quayside to be stealthily unloaded and hidden in the Hole in the Wall, until they could be safely dispatched by a carrier along some lonely Wealden track to London.

The Codiham Gang of smugglers was notorious not only for its tricking of the excise men, but for the manner in which it terrorized the district. Its members had a particularly unpleasant method of dealing with informants. Once caught, the informer was taken to Ghost's Wood where he was first castrated, then tarred and feathered and tied to a tree. The howls of the demented victims are said to have been so terrible that people swore the wood was haunted, hence the sinister name applied to this eerie little coppice now happily only populated at night by owls.

The Hole in the Wall was the headquarters of the Codiham Gang; in fact the cellar which forms the bar of the present public house was the secret cache of the smugglers. When the Codiham Gang were 'in the money', however, they celebrated at the Bearpits. The excise men would search the latter and forget all about the less-fashionable 'Hole'. At the back of the Bearpits, adjoining what are now marbles beds, is Bearpits Lane, a narrow, winding alley which was, in the eighteenth century, the haunt of many dubious sportsmen, pickpockets and gamblers. Sir Walter Thyme, the wild, rake-hell squire of the mid-eighteenth century, not only encouraged bear-baiting, but purchased bears for this purpose. It is on record that a Codiham butcher, named Richard Staton, was fined 3s. 4d. in 1758 for killing a bear without first 'baiting it according to custom'. Whether he intended to substitute bear-steaks for beef-steaks is not known.

Sir Walter, the patron-in-chief of this disgusting sport (he was killed in a duel), bequeathed a house, the annual rent of which was £8, to provide one bear annually to be baited in the Codiham Bear Ring. The great day for baiting was St. Thomas's Day; the ceremony opened with the arrival of the Squire and his rakish companions. The bear's nose was filled with pepper to enrage it; then, with a fifteen-foot chain attached, it was fixed to a ring and the first dog was let loose on it. Staffordshire terriers seem to have been used rather than bull-dogs, and local farmers often found their bulls missing when some of the Codiham Gang, who owned most of the dogs, took it into their heads to give the animals some practice at night. The tenacity of the dogs must have been amazing, for it is recorded that the owner of one such dog won a bet by cutting off each of his dog's legs in succession without the dog letting go of the bear's nose!

Cock-fighting was also indulged in at the Bearpits and on one occasion Sir Walter created a diversion by bringing women into the pits to fight one another; they were stripped to the waist and, to discourage them from scratching each other's eyes out, forced to hold a silver coin in each hand.

'The wickedness of Codiham,' said one eighteenth-century scribe, 'must be witnessed to be believed. It is a sink, a stew and a raging Inferno of vice, with cock-fighting, bear-baiting, licentiousness and drunkenness from sunrise to long after midnight.'

Sir Walter left one lasting memory to the village. Having paid a visit to Italy, he became enamoured of Palladian architecture and the current fashion for elaborate gardens. He had long since spent all his own money so he decided to sacrifice himself on the altar and married the fat and extremely dowdy daughter of a wealthy London alderman. He consoled himself with her dowry, adding Palladian arches and a terrace to the Tudor manor house and thereby altering its whole character. Over the moat he constructed a Palladian bridge and in the grounds he designed a curiously erotic garden. Both the bridge and garden still remain and week-end visitors to Codiham in July and August pay half-crowns to see them. The garden has been a great blessing to the present squire and Lord of the Manor, who has managed to combat the erosion of death duties by throwing open the house and grounds to the public in these months.

It has not been possible, however, to retain all the erotica introduced by the rakish Sir Walter. True, some statues of fauns, satyrs and nymphs still bear tribute to his single-minded passion for the chase – whether of animals or women. It is also possible to recognize that on the northern slope of the gardens a certain plot is cunningly laid out in the likeness of a nude woman pursued by a rampant Bacchus: statuary and bushes, artificial mounds and tapering stone paths have been cleverly arranged to give this effect. But some of the ruder mottoes in crude, Macaroni Latin which Sir Walter had inscribed on trees, the obscene Temple of Bacchus and the lewder figures in the grottoes have been removed and replaced by rose-beds and rhododendron bushes.

The Thymes maintained their reputation as a rollicking, hell-daring family until well on in the nineteenth century. One was killed at the Battle of the Nile, another lost his life in the Peninsular War. But when Sebastian Thyme took holy orders in 1883 the villagers shook their heads and feared that the legend that 'a Thyme never dies with his boots off' had been finally destroyed. Sebastian, however, was made of equally stern, if more virtuous stuff. An ardent evangelist, he was murdered by cannibals in the South Seas whence he had gone to convert them. Thus did history seek its own revenge on the worst of all the Thymes, that baby-devouring monster whose tomb lies in Saint Mildred's Church, and the moral of this coincidence was not lost upon Codiham's inhabitants. Since this date squires of Codiham have lost their lives in the Boer War, the First World War and in the Tunisian campaign of 1943. The present baronet, Sir Oswald Thyme, has publicly gone on record that he sincerely hopes to demolish the legend for all time by dying comfortably in his bed. For showing such levity and appearing to challenge a cherished Codiham tradition, he is regarded in the village as an iconoclast and 'a bit of a Bolshie', an allegation which in the minds of some villagers has been confirmed by the fact that he actually speaks Russian.

In fact, Sir Oswald is a strange mixture of the radical and the conservative: he was rejected by one Conservative Association as a prospective candidate because he holds strong views against hanging. On the other hand he is an ardent fighter against bureaucracy wherever it raises its head unreasonably, or attempts to encroach on ancient human rights. He prefers to keep fairly independent politically, or, as he prefers to put it, to 'dine with the Tories and drink with the Socialists'. He has been known to drive a cricket ball off the Green through one of the Merry Damsel windows (a feat not equalled this century, says Young George) and he has done much to break down the idea that a squire is a man apart. He cannot afford to hunt, as did his ancestors, nor does this worry him, but Flossie at the Hole in the Wall often tells how he played 'Sailor' Thompsett at darts one night and then entertained the whole assembly on the piano.

His one extravagance is sailing, which partly explains his fondness for 'Sailor' Thompsett, whom he takes with him on a foreign cruise once a year in his very modest yacht. Cucking Manor was far too large for him to maintain in its entirety, so he has given over the ballroom and various other parts of the building to such local organizations as the Codiham Amateur Dramatic Society, the Women's Institute and the British Legion, also converting the lodge into a local museum. Squire Sir Oswald is yet another example of how leadership can enthuse a community and how privilege properly used can still make a contribution in the Age of the Welfare State.

Politically, Codiham is an odd place, and well worth special study. Its native 'wickedness' throughout the ages enabled it to change its colours as frequently as the Vicar of Bray, yet it has always had a reputation for being 'agin the Government' and of defying authority, not to mention downright cussedness. Codiham's Parish Council, probably due to the fact that until the reign of Elizabeth I it was quite an important body, is much more party-minded than that of most villages. There is no nonsense about Independents, Municipal Reformers, or Progressives. The candidates are either Tories, Labourites or Liberals, practically without exception; anyone calling himself an Independent would be suspect in Codiham. Except for the Liberal hey-day of 1906–10, the Parish Council has always had a Tory majority. But the trends in these elections are especially interesting and a snub to any public opinion pollster. In 1931, when the *Morning Post* announced that Labour was 'sunk without trace', the Labour vote in the Parish Council elections went up and the Tory vote decreased. In 1945, when it was Labour's turn to sweep the country, the Tory vote went up and the Labour vote went down. You can generally bet that Codiham will always go against the national trend.

It is possibly true that in many villages the green either is, or has been the centre of its social life. But though Cucking Green is the geographical centre-piece of Codiham, the analogy does not apply. Codiham has traditionally regarded its green as a kind of verdant sanctuary, the very reverse of any suggestion of communal life. It is for this reason that Cucking Green remains an English jungle of trees, bushes and narrow paths, why it has never been transformed into one of those charming, yet rather artificial village greens of close-clipped grass and wide open spaces. Similarly, the main streets forming the triangular boundary of the Green have never been invaded with club houses, institutes and working men's clubs.

From time to time the question of 'cropping the Green' has been ventilated by a few cranks on the Parish Council. But whenever Cucking Green has been threatened in this manner an esoteric telepathy has provoked the great mass of Codgemites to protest against such measures in unison. Partly the protest has always had aesthetic roots: a wooded, jungly green in sweet disorder has appealed to people rather as a sanctified zone of freedom. Codiham likes to feel it can 'pop across the Green and have a real laze' and, more important, the welcome shade and seclusion which only the trees can supply.

Of course, 'wickedness' has played its part. The 'cuckers', the bussers, the Green-walkers, the work dodgers and the poachers have always preferred to frolic, snare, court and what-you-will in the jungle. Cucking Green still is the rendezvous of amorous young villagers – not necessarily the same thing as 'cuckers' – and in smuggling days the hollows of old oaks were favourite hiding-places for kegs of brandy.

In the nineteenth century a puritanically minded vicar wanted to 'remove all the trees from the Green and by so doing to drive out god-lessness which doth flourish thereon like the trees themselves'. He also wished to remove Miranda's font from Saint Mildred's Church. Neither wish was fulfilled.

This same vicar was a protagonist of that school of muscular Christianity which regards sport as next to godliness and almost a substitute for deeper theology. He believed that 'by cropping the Green, we shall cleanse it of "much perilous stuff" and can as a result substitute manly sports for more dubious pastimes'. Being a determined and strong-willed character, though defeated on the major issues, he pushed through one revolutionary project – the creation of a cricket pitch.

Codiham, accustomed to so many other less-disciplined pastimes, had not until that date – 1854 – succumbed to village cricket. Bear-baiting had lasted until the early days of the nineteenth century and stoolball had been played in desultory fashion in fields near Half-Naked Farm. In Sir Walter Thyme's hey-day that rapscallion squire, aided and abetted by his friend, the Earl of Sandwich, sometimes referred to as 'the wickedest man in England', had introduced cricket to the grounds of Cucking Manor. But it was left to the puritanical vicar to teach Codiham cricket. At first his efforts were resented; then, amazed at his capacity for hard hitting and fast bowling, the villagers' hostility turned to reluctant admiration, then cautious enjoyment of the new sport.

In Saint Mildred's Churchyard is a tombstone bearing the inscription:

> In memory of NICHOLAS HONEYBUN, M.A., B.D.,
> vicar of this parish, 1848–1871.
> Famed for his forthright opinions,
> integrity and sincerity.
> He was also the founder of cricket in
> Codiham and the originator of
> over-arm bowling.

It is a matter of controversy in the Weald as to who really invented over-arm bowling. In Kent they say the originator was one John Willes, whose tombstone at Sutton Valance claims he was the inventor of 'round-arm bowling'. Nonsense, says Codiham, round-arm bowling is not the same thing; our Reverend Nicholas bowled over-arm when every other village side in these parts could only serve up schoolgirlish under-arms. Certainly the Reverend Nicholas fought a long battle in favour of over-arm bowling, though he may not have emulated John Willes by going up to Lords to state his case. To prove his point he and a fellow clergyman challenged a Codiham XI to a match – two against eleven. It was played on the Green in 1856; Codiham scored 29 all out and the two clerics carried their bats for 33, thus winning by ten wickets. The score-card of this memorable game is framed in the Cricket Club's pavilion. I cannot help feeling it should be kept somewhere safer, for it marked the last occasion on which a Codiham side ever bowled under-arm.

Cricket, despite the Reverend Nicholas's pious hopes, did not oust 'cucking', kissing and bussing as the youthful villagers' main pastime. With smuggling a thing of the past, with stoolball now regarded as purely a woman's game, cricket and drinking were merely complementary to the ancient amorous recreations. As though in defiance of the one open space on Cucking Green, 'cucking' was actually conducted in the primitive shelter and open pavilion which first graced the Cricket Club's allotted plot. The entwined hearts and initials which formerly only appeared on tree trunks were now carved on the pavilion walls. Stern action had to be taken to check this and the Reverend Nicholas preached almost Calvinistic sermons in denouncing the 'cuckers' and shocked his congregation by using this word in the pulpit. Perhaps it was as well he didn't live to see Mafeking Night when, according to a country newspaper report, 'there were disgraceful scenes of drunkenness and debauchery on Cucking Green, culminating in charges being heard at a special police court. Because of the excuse for the celebrations lenient sentences were imposed.'

By the beginning of the twentieth century there was little industry remaining in Codiham. Hop-growing and fruit-farming were the chief occupations, though at the disused quayside by the River Dentical old Robert Turley still carried on boat-building until 1911. A few individual craftsmen survived. Jeremiah Jephson, at the age of eighty-three, even today makes the most exquisite reproductions of Queen Anne furniture which, as a youth, he studied in the South Kensington Museum. He is a natural wood-worker, contemptuous of modern copyists and strongly disapproves of the shine put on furniture by professional polishers. He himself prefers to rub in beeswax and then, with the impetus of a good deal of elbow-grease, to put on a little French polish. And the village baker, working in the Tudor shop-front of his ancestors, still bakes Codgem Cakes, a relic of Elizabethan times when they were distributed to the poor on Maundy Thursday.

These are hot gingerbread cakes, topped with gay icing patterns of shining gold. 'That,' says the baker, 'is how we got the saying about taking the gilt off the gingerbread.'

Well, it may be so. History is created in a variety of ways and even a baker's shop may supply a clue to a great deal of it, just as the Reverend Nicholas Honeybun's tombstone tells of a revolution in cricket. Codiham is not likely to see a revival of industry in its neighbourhood, which is all to the good for that would destroy its character. But Sir Oswald Thyme is doing his best to encourage and recreate old craftsmanship. What the village has lost in industry since the passing of the silk-worms and the hammer ponds, it has gained in artistic pursuits. Codiham may be no more or no less philistinistic than most villages – certainly no one would hope to achieve much here if he breathed the dread, ugly Teutonic word, culture – but it has taken one class of 'furriner' to its bosom – the artists.

We shall hear more about this small section of the community later. It will suffice now to say that after the 1914–18 war a few artists 'discovered' Codiham. Perhaps luckily they were not famous artists, nor were they particularly commercially-minded, otherwise the village might have degenerated into a rather phoney paradise with olde worlde tea-shops and bogus Bohemiana. They were mainly amateurs content to settle in Codiham and adapt themselves to the villagers' ways.

Not that they didn't possess the Bohemian touch, but it was the

.Bohemianism of poverty and simplicity rather than that of a cult. It was an unpretentious spirit which fitted in very well with the blue-sweatered, clay-piped democracy of the Hole in the Wall, where many a water-colour, or crayon sketch, fixed in the walls, has been done to pay for a drink bill. Retired fishermen, farm labourers and artists could rejoice together in the fact that 'us be proper wicked down at Codgem'.

This chapter may not be everyone's idea of history. I have tried by copious research in the tiny museum to give as accurate a picture as possible of the evolution of the village, but, as legends are usually infinitely more amusing than fact, I have included many which a pro-fessional historian would probably reject. Yet even a don could hardly claim that Codiham did not provide ample material for a broad picture of English country life over the centuries – one which explains many of our national foibles, our gift of laughing at ourselves, our weaknesses and our strengths, and, above all, the abiding continuity of purpose. Sometimes the purpose may have been inspired more by the devils than the angels. But, generally speaking, it would be more charitable to say that Puck predominated over prudery, that even the 'wickedness' has been mellowed through tolerance and experience into something approaching a civilized way of life.

6. In which Codiham United signs a French philanderer

It was not until ten months later that we eventually came to live in the oast house on Cucking Green. Bad weather had delayed much of the work of conversion and, as we had not employed an architect, the whole project was one of slow progress through trial and error. We worked out amateurish sketches of what we wanted done, then took them along to Dick Pride, the builder. Dick was an extremely tolerant professional who politely ignored our more outrageous misconceptions of what could and could not be done. He merely sipped his pint of ale, drew another sketch and added: 'I think we'll get what you want if we do it like this.'

'This', of course, was something quite different, yet in an astonishing way it did work out more or less as we wanted.

The work went on long after we had settled in. Almost every day we discovered some new snag, some other problem that required ironing out. All the same there were certain problems which we just had to learn to live with. One of these was the question of narrow stair-treads. It was important not to waste too much space and this had resulted in a very narrow stair-case up the roundel. But we quickly got used to these by the simple process of walking upstairs sideways. This may sound awkward and laborious; in fact, it is probably the easiest way to save your breath and narrow stairs are far less tiring to climb than stairs with wide treads.

We were soon to learn that Codiham, though it regarded 'furriners' with some suspicion, had an eye to the main chance. If a 'furriner' wished to be accepted in the village, he had to show he was prepared to some extent to be exploited. Thus the only people who called on us in those early days were those who wished – well, to put it bluntly – to make use of us.

It was late August when we arrived in Codiham – not the best time to start life in the country. One is too easily lured from the harsher, sterner tasks by the innumerable delights around one – the swans on the pond, the seductive smells of freshly mown grass from Cucking Green, the lattice-work of innumerable tree branches forming a Gothic roof above one's head. But no sooner has one slipped into a deck-chair to indulge in such simple pleasures than there comes a call to duty; some furniture requires shifting, there's the question of whether one more packing-case can be put up in the loft, or if that water-colour in the hall is hanging properly.

But almost every month has its drawbacks for setting up home in the country. In November there are fogs and an air of decay and dank, mouldering vegetation: everywhere seems damp. After Christmas is a depressing time anyhow and one wishes only to huddle round a fire. Spring may seem traditionally the perfect month, but it presents the problem of coping with the garden which at that time is pressing and unpostponable. So perhaps August is no worse than any other month.

Dick Pride began to get restless in August and to mutter darkly about having 'more important things to do'. At first I couldn't imagine what he meant by these vague statements, but gradually the truth came out. Dick was not only a parish councillor, but a man with a fanatical ambition which, to do him justice, gave him a geat deal of unpaid work and cost him quite a lot of money. That ambition was to make Codiham United Football Club the finest village side in the whole of Sussex. It was a subject which, like King Charles's head, became an obsession.

Yet he didn't flaunt his secret passion. And I am quite sure that Dick must have cut down his estimates of some of the jobs he did for us simply because I showed a polite interest in the club of which he was chairman.

The story of Codiham United fascinated me because it seemed to be the symbol of the history of all British football. It isn't the composer of a brilliant concerto who lays the foundations of the culture of a nation but the peasants with their folk-songs and mummery. And so with football: the Arsenals may carve a classic pattern and exude the glamour of gladiatorial exhibitionism, but what gives the game its wide appeal is due almost entirely to the thousands of small clubs whose names are rarely heard of outside their immediate vicinity.

One evening Dick Pride showed me a pile of ancient and dusty minute books, faded yellow press cuttings and photographs of long-since dead stalwarts of Codiham football. I think it was this peep into the past which caused me to take something more than a polite interest in his main ambition. As I mentioned in the last chapter the village's football club was founded under the title of Codiham Cannibals in 1872. Their colours were scarlet and gold, with a skull and crossbones–in deference to the legend of Sir Jervis Thyme – embroidered on their shirts. The colours and the emblem remain the same to this day, despite the fact that the name 'Cannibals' has been dropped and the piratical badge, though used unofficially on supporters' home-made banners, no longer adorns the shirt-pocket. In the 'nineties the Vicar of Codiham was president of the club and he managed to get the name changed to Codiham United when the Cannibals were merged with two younger clubs – Codiham Thursday and Saint Mildred's Wanderers.

Players in the 'seventies were drawn almost exclusively from what in those rather class-conscious days were called 'the landed gentry'. The public schools' retreat from soccer had not then been sounded and it was the long-trousered, bewhiskered, nonchalant ex-public schoolboys and sons of the gentry who wore the scarlet and gold colours of the Cannibals. They played on a pitch in a hollow at the end of Silk Lane, known locally as the Devil's Frying Pan. You can never go far in Codiham without finding some reference to the Devil and his works.

Codiham Thursday and Saint Mildred's Wanderers were formed, not as rivals to the Cannibals, but to give the ordinary village boy a chance to play football. But lack of funds and a decline in snobbery brought about a merger of the three clubs, the Cannibals supplying most of the money and the other two clubs a more varied array of talent. Soccer could never have become the highly organized and cultured game it is today, but for the selfless devotion of its junior players more than half a century ago. They not only paid their subscriptions, but their travelling fares as well and more often than not the more affluent members dipped into their pockets to make up an end-of-the-season deficit. But by 1912 finances must have been improving for it is recorded in the minutes of the annual meeting for that year that 'it was agreed to make a grant of 9*d.* per match to be spent on half-time refreshment for players'. That was approved, though doubtless a few diehards of the old school muttered that the younger generation was becoming soft.

'What about your coming along to one of our meetings?' asked Dick Pride one evening.

'Well, I'm not even a member yet,' I said.

'I can soon put that right. You've only got to pay half a crown to be a member.'

Half a crown, I thought, was neither here, nor there. Much less expensive than joining a golf club and thereby consorting with week-end business men from London. After all I had come to the country to escape from all that. Added to which there was the attraction that the United's headquarters were at the Hole in the Wall.

So that was how I became involved in the fortunes of Codiham United Football Club. Dick Pride made me a member and took me along to one of the meetings. Of course, it wasn't just a matter of half a crown. Flossie Whitcombe quickly informed me that she was president of the Supporters' Club and would I like to speculate a bob a week on their pools' scheme. Before the evening was ended Flossie Whitcombe had proposed and Dick Pride had seconded that I be elected a vice-president. Which meant a further subscription.

'Sir Oswald Thyme is president of the club and the vicar, the doctor and Fitworth, the bank manager, are vice-presidents, so you'll be in good company,' said Dick.

But the real work of any football club in these expensive days is done by the Supporters' Club. It is a mistake to believe that only wealthy professional teams have the backing of such organizations. If a village side has any ambitions at all, it must have its Supporters' Club and Flossie Whitcombe, that red-headed dynamo of a pub-keeper, was in my opinion the driving force behind Codiham football. If Dick Pride was the man with a vision, the cool business head for planning bigger things, Flossie was the money-raiser. She organized weekly whist drives, a football pool's tote, dances, musical evenings and even a miniature Venetian Carnival on the River Dentical every summer, all in aid of the United.

I never regretted allowing myself to be coaxed into joining this happy little club, for, prosaic as it may sound, it was a never-ending source of fun, excitement and worth-while endeavour. I think, too, that it was my first positive step towards improving my status as a 'furriner'. An author is always suspect in Britain; writing is regarded as, if not a form of madness, at least a peculiarity. The few authors who had flitted in and out of the Codiham scene had been 'pretty queer fish', according to forthright 'Sailor' Thompsett.

I came to Codiham just as the village team was being resurrected from – this is Flossie Whitcombe speaking – 'a fate worse than death'. When the war ended, it became very difficult to raise a village side. National Service meant that promising youngsters were soon lost; full employment with plenty of overtime, the attractions of 'the telly' and the demand of youth to get paid for whatever they did aggravated the situation. Some youths hinted broadly that they wouldn't play unless they had adequate 'expenses'. 'So-and-So Rovers will pay me two quid a week as an amateur,' was their cry.

Codiham United had a debt of £62; the bank threatened to foreclose on their overdraft as soon as the credit squeeze began. There was no question of being able to afford to pay any such 'expenses', but, even had that been possible (not to mention its illegality in amateur football), Dick Pride was adamant that it would only be done 'over my dead body. If you want to play for So-and-So Rovers, you can bloody well b—— off and do so.'

But genuine amateurs were few and so the United went from one disaster to another. In 1955 they finished bottom of the South Weald League, having lost every match they played, with only 9 goals in their favour and 148 against. To me this seemed a magnificent achievement, and I am not being sarcastic. When a club is so much in debt that it cannot even pay its players' travelling expenses, when these same players have a whip-round for £12 to save the club from extinction half-way through the season, when they lose week after week – sometimes by such scores as 0–21 – and occasionally call on a veteran of fifty to help them out, it says much for the sportsmanship and resolution of all concerned.

It was then that Dick Pride took charge. He called an extraordinary general meeting and launched a campaign for funds, using his personal influence to persuade people to give both time and money. 'Bring in the ladies,' was Dick's shrewd battle cry. 'The ladies'll love it. There's Miss Ablethorpe down at The Limes. Her father was captain of the old Cannibals and used to play for the county. We can count on her for a good sub, if we make her a vice-president. And Flossie, now – that bundle of energy's just itching to do something.'

Dick personally paid off the overdraft at the bank and stormed into the manager's office to tell him in no uncertain terms what he could do with his 'services'. 'You're a perishin' old misery,' he added, 'trying to make our old football club pack up. And our account is going elsewhere.'

Crafty Dick waited until he had persuaded the manager of the rival bank in Codiham to become a vice-president of the club before he embarrassed that gentleman by offering him the club's account.

'Oh, really,' said the bank manager over a drink at the Merry Damsel, 'I don't mind helping the club. After all I'm an old soccer man myself. But I don't like the idea of taking business away from old Carshalton. During the "squeeze" we're not supposed to do this sort of thing, you know. Rather smacks of unfair competition.'

'Unfair my perishin' foot!' grunted Dick. 'Unfair to Codiham, that's what it is. What are banks for but competition? You might as well nationalize 'em, if you're going to take that line. I ain't asking you for an overdraft. I've told you, we've paid that off.'

'Oh, very well then,' replied the manager, probably fearing that Dick would withdraw his own not inconsiderable account if he offered further opposition.

That was merely the beginning of the revival. 'If we've lost every bloomin' match,' said Dick, 'it's because we haven't had enough training. What we want is a training pitch so as we don't cut up our own pitch down at the Devil's Frying Pan. Darned if I won't tackle old Perrywiggle who owns the field at the back of the Frying Pan.'

In this manner Dick bullied, cajoled and coaxed nearly the whole of Codiham into helping him to achieve his ambition. Old Perrywiggle took some persuading, but eventually agreed to lend his field for twice-weekly training sessions. Only the geese he kept there voiced their protest when a white ball came whistling among them like a missile from outer space in the dusk of a late August evening. Codiham United had never done any serious training before and the idea of exercise under the supervision of the ex-sergeant-major and P.T. instructor who was Dick Pride's chief assistant made them apprehensive.

'Making us work like bloody convicts,' grumbled centre-forward Bill Blurge. 'Might as well ask us to join the Army.'

'Listen, young Blurge,' said Dick. 'Your trouble's your left foot. Proper *larmentable* shot you got with un and that's summat you've got to conquer. If you get practisin' with your left foot of a night, I reckon you might double your goal tally.'

After three sessions under the instructions of the fiery P.T. expert the players called a protest meeting. 'We ain't in no bloody war,' said one. 'Any more of this and we're goin' to strike.'

Undismayed, Dick himself spoke to the rebels. 'Let's get this straight,' he said. 'If you don't want to train, you needn't play at all. I'm not going to let you go out on the Devil's Fryin' Pan week after week to be licked by a cricket score. Making you all the laughing stock of the district. You stick out the training for a month and I'll stand you a sausage, mash and beer supper when you get your first win. Once you start winning, you'll feel different about this training stuff.'

'Sounds fair enough to me,' replied Bill Blurge. 'But how can we dribble a perishin' white ball round a row of stakes of a night when the only light we've got is the headlamps of two vans?'

'I'll take care of that,' answered Dick. 'I'll fix you up with a couple of arc-lights which we'll hoist on some of old Perrywiggle's hop-poles.'

'What about our wives and girl friends?' asked Bill Blurge, always the most vocal member of the team. 'My Lill says she's fed up 'anging around on 'er own two nights a week. She ull fair razzle[1] me if it goes on.'

'Tell you what I'll do,' said Dick, his favourite expression for starting any sentence, from explaining how he would put in a new window to dealing with recalcitrant footballers. 'Tell you what I'll do – I'll build a club-house at the far end of Devil's Fryin' Pan, the Perrywiggle's field end, and we'll get the Supporters' Club to open it up on training nights for the ladies to wait in and have a cup of tea.'

'That's mighty generous of you, Mr. Pride,' said Bill Blurge. 'I reckon you'll just about save me from being told to adone-do by my Lill. And Charlie Denman's missus 'as bin fair razzling 'im since he got 'ome late after that match at Ninfield. She wouldn't believe the coach broke down.'

'No more would my Belinda,' chipped in Jim Bricknell, the United left-back and the village's grave-digger.

'Serves you right for carrying on with a party with one of them film-star, fancy names,' was Bill Blurge's caustic comment.

'If you fellows was to pay as much attention to doubling round Perrywiggle's field and dribbling round the stakes as you do to getting so vlothered[2] about the girls, you might start winning a few matches,' remarked ex-Sergeant Major Sam Perkins, formerly of the Royal Marines.

'You're jealous, that's wot you are, Sarn't-Major,' teased Bill Blurge, who was the bane of Sam Perkins's life.

Before the P.T.I. could explode with sergeant-majorly indignation at the laughter which greeted this sally, Clive Harrison-Tracey, the outside-right, switched the conversation by suggesting: 'Do we really want our

[1] *Razzle* means 'to speak up in an abusive manner'.
[2] *Vlothered* means 'worked up'.

camp followers hanging around while we are training? Isn't the whole idea of football to escape from their clutches for a while? And, what is more, isn't it cheaper to slip off to the Hole in the Wall after training without having them tagging along?'

'All right for you,' said Charlie Denman. 'You're a ruddy bachelor, and when you want a bit of crumpet, you just pop over to Brighton in your Bentley.'

'Now, lads,' said Dick Pride. 'I'm sure we don't want to confuse the issue. Before I put this question of training to the vote – and I can hardly be more democratic than that – I should like to say that we will find an answer to all your problems. I'll see you get those arc lights. I won't forget about the celebration supper – *when* you've won. I'll see you get a club-house, though you'll probably have to help build it. As for the problem of the ladies, well, if Clive wants to escape from 'em and go down to the Hole on his own, it's a free world and there's no reason why he shouldn't. We all know he disappears to Brighton each Wednesday night. But I agree with the majority of you that the ladies are all important. That's why I've tried to get the ladies interested in the club. Make 'em feel at home. Let 'em join in the fun.

'I don't want to see any happy homes broken up just because after an away match you stop at a pub and have a few drinks and get home late. For years it has been a strict rule that there should be no ladies in the team coach. Well, I think that's a silly rule and should be scrapped. Let 'em all come, if they want to. Wives, girl friends, mothers and even mothers-in-law.'

'Oh, no!' groaned Clive.

But Dick won his way.

.   .   .   .   .

A few weeks later Sylvia and I were walking back to the oast house from the Merry Damsel one night when we overheard a strange conversation as we crossed Cucking Green.

'Not as yet. I doan't like to go about things so quickly,' pleaded a young Sussex maid from the hollow of an oak.

'Well, that's all right by me,' was the reply in the unmistakable accents of young Harrison-Tracey. 'I don't mind staying up until two in the morning if it suits you.'

'I maun get back home afore eleven. It's too cold to stay out longer anyhow.'

'Ah, well, in that case we'd better lose no time.'

'Adone! Adone-do!'

'Don't cackle, girl. Nobody's done anything to you yet.'

There was silence for a few seconds. Then, in a soft, cooing, less-agitated tone of voice, came a whispered: 'Oh! do adone!'

'What on earth does she mean?' asked Sylvia when we were out of earshot of the couple. 'It sounds like something out of Shakespeare.'

'It undoubtedly is,' I replied. 'Or at least very much the same language as they used in Shakespeare's time. I am told that "adone" means "leave off. Don't do it." "Adone-do" means "Stop it immediately" and "Do adone" means "Please go on".'

'Do what? Don't do what? And please go on with what?'

'That,' I replied, 'I must leave to your imagination.'

'You seem to have learned an uncanny amount about the habits and sayings of lovelorn Sussex maidens,' said Sylvia tartly.

'Adone-do,' I added.

'Well, Clive Harrison-Tracey seems to have adone pretty well for himself. I thought you said he was the chap who voted against having girls in the team coach.'

'Correct.'

'What a hypocrite!'

'Oh, come now, he didn't pretend to be a misogynist. As a matter of fact I rather think last Saturday's coach trip found him a new girl friend.'

'Well, he can hardly call that training.'

.   .   .   .   .

Dick Pride's policy of 'bringing in the ladies' was, however, a tremendous success. There were some who said it was 'against the best interests of sport'. Sam Perkins was one of those. There were other pessimists who said it would lead to 'no end of trouble. The women ull squabble and start trying to pick the team.' 'They'll stop us drinking on the way home.' 'Bill Blurge's Lill ull sure to start making sheep's eyes at that handsome Harrison-Tracey fellow.'

But the ladies succeeded not only in being civilized themselves, but in civilizing the men. Bill Blurge, who could hardly open his mouth without a string of obscene four-letter words pouring forth, was severely curbed by Lill. Clive Harrison-Tracey, despite his agricultural college background, was a true democrat really and he soon found consolation in the presence in the coach parties of the postman's daughter. Charlie

Denman's missus, who had hitherto been regarded as a 'bit of a shrew', positively revelled in being taken into a pub on the way back from away matches and being treated to Baby Chams – 'see they put a cherry in it.'

The greatest stalwart of these outings was Flossie Whitcombe. She wore an enormous scarlet and gold rosette and even had an umbrella in the club colours. Flossie was doubly welcome because she brought along sandwiches and a flask of tea. Saturday was Flossie's 'day off' in the winter. She never reckoned to go behind the bar in her own pub until the coach arrived back at the Hole in the Wall. She had a strident voice that matched her red hair and opponents must have blanched when she bellowed: 'Up Codgem! Come along my lucky lads! Get stuck into 'em and give 'em merry hell!'

'I must say,' Dick Pride told me with awe one day, 'Flossie's support at any match is worth a goal to us.'

And soon enough – whether due to the training sessions or to the support of the ladies – goals began to come and Codiham won a match at last. Sam Perkins continued with his stern exhortations to 'train, train, train till you bloody well drop' and though Bill Blurge grumbled he scored a hat-trick against Pangham, actually getting the last goal with a deft hook of his suspect left foot.

On Tuesdays and Thursdays, under the arc lights on the hop-poles in Perrywiggle's field, while the geese hissed angrily, the footballers of Codiham, breathing barrel-chestfuls of chill, night air, went pounding round in circles, kicking, trapping, dribbling round stakes, practising corner-kicks and shedding excess fat. 'Sprint now. Keep your knees up to your chin! Double up there, Blurge, and use that blasted left foot more. Here, Denman, stop wriggling as though you were a monkey sitting on a pile of tin-tacks!' bellowed Sam Perkins.

A new spirit actuated the whole club. On one training week-night Lady Thyme drove down to Perrywiggle's field with Thermos flasks of hot coffee and sandwiches for the players and any girl friends and wives who might have braved the cold to stand about under the arc lights. And meanwhile, Dick Pride set about getting materials for the new club-house.

One evening when I popped into the Hole in the Wall I found Flossie and 'Sailor' Thompsett in earnest conversation. 'Sailor', I soon discovered, was a man of many activities, with a great love of intrigue. The more complicated and full of intrigue any kind of business was, the more 'Sailor' enjoyed it. Since the war he had only been a part-time fisherman, but he had eked out a livelihood by a variety of means – fishing, when he felt like it and when the weather was suitable; organizing trips up the Channel in his small craft, *Dainty Doris*, during July and August; a certain amount of smuggling (or at least, so we suspected); dealing in scrap iron; extra for a film company which occasionally operated on Romney Marsh.

These must have been his chief means of earning a living, but there were many other lucrative sidelines as well. Certainly finding houses for prospective buyers was another, though 'Sailor' was happy enough to be paid for this in beer and rum from whatever middle-man, or agent he acted for. It was whispered that in the days of rationing immediately after the war he was the village's principal supplier of nylons. He never gave the impression of having a lot of money, though his daily round of Codiham's three pubs must have cost him plenty, for he was never a cadger and always stood his round. Yet it was said that he had more than £200 in Premium Bonds. His most recent side line was acting as chief talent spotter for Codiham United. And I rather think that in some devious manner he made this honorary and entirely unofficial post lucrative.

'Dick Pride's told me I must find a new goalkeeper, an inside-left and another full-back,' he was telling Flossie.

'Do you mean to say you can't find anybody in the village?' asked Flossie.

'Well, if you count Henty[1] in the village, I've found a jolly good full-back there. Trouble is he works at Hastings and we shall have to fix transport for him. But that's not what I came to talk to you about. Dunnamany footballers I've given the once over. Proper scoured the area for talent and, what's more, I've even taken a look across the Channel.'

'Across the Channel, "Sailor"? What with those Froggies?'

'That's right, Floss, my luvvy, and I reckon I've found a goalkeeper in France.'

'But how the heck do you think a Froggie is going to pop over here of a Saturday afternoon to play for Codgem? Who's going to pay his expenses?'

'Ah, that's where you come in, Flossie.'

'The Supporters' Club ain't paying for any fancy Froggie to come over here and play once a week. You must be out of your mind, "Sailor".'

'Now, listen, sweetheart. This Froggie chap is a bloomin' miracle

A hamlet just outside Codiham, derived from *hen* and *tye*, meaning a common.

man. And we want a new goalkeeper badly. Old Jerry's played for us since 1938 and he can't get down to the low shots now – too stiff in the joints. A few weeks ago I went over to Boulogne for a jaunt – never mind why, I just went for my 'ealth, see. There was a football match with this Froggie playin'. His name is L'Amour – know wot that is, don't you, ducky? He's a smasher to look at, only twenty-two and a real dark and 'andsome one.'

'We want a goalkeeper, not a gigolo.'

'Well, this Froggie is a goalkeeper in a million. He's a ruddy acrobat when it comes to stopping difficult shots. So I made pals with him, see. My French is about 'arf a dozen phrases – *comment*, *bon jour*, *combien* and *promenez-vous avec moi, ma'm'selle?* and stuff like that. But wot with my bit of French and 'is knowing a tidy bit of English, we got on fine. And the upshot of it all, Flossie, is that he wants more'n anything else to get a job as a barman in England. "Get me a job in your village," he says, "and I'll play for your football team." So, as I just said, that's where you come in, Flossie. Can you give 'im a job?'

'What here? My customers at the Hole ull never a-bear[1] a furriner, and no one knows that better'n you, "Sailor".'

'Well, he's too good to let slip. Classy young fellow. Just right for a cocktail-bar job. Knows the names of all those fancy drinks and can mix a dry martin, or whatever they call it. What about the Damsel?'

'I can't very well ask Mr. Pargetter.'

'What about you, Mr. McCormick?' said 'Sailor', pointing his clay pipe in my direction. 'You get on very well with old Pargetter. Why, he even let you and your missus sleep in that bed of Mad Miranda's. No disrespect meant, but if you could get Pargetter to do that, you could get him to do anything.'

Obviously our occupation of the King's Damsel's Bed had been village gossip.

'I suppose, as a vice-president, I can hardly refuse,' I replied. 'But he's not going to take anybody on without seeing him first.'

'I'll 'ave 'im over here in double quick time, if you can wrestle even half a promise out of Pargetter.'

And so it was that I became personally involved in a scheme to bring a star French goalkeeper over to Codiham. I explained the situation to Mr. Pargetter, who, though a keen supporter of the village cricket club, was not a soccer man. Cautiously he promised to agree to an interview with the young Frenchman, but would not commit himself more than that.

[1] Endure, put up with.

'We could do with some help in the summer months, but I'm a bit doubtful about having a barman named L'Amour. I can see that being a real problem,' he said. 'It's bad enough being called the Merry Damsel and having Miranda's Bed. But a barman named L'Amour into the bargain. . . . I just don't know.'

I carefully avoided making the point that 'Sailor' Thompset had wished me to put to Pargetter – that, as Mrs. Pargetter was French, this should obviate all difficulties. I felt that any such reference was irrelevant and probably tactless.

Sylvia thought that a French barman might well prove a decided asset at the Merry Damsel. 'An English pub and a handsome French barman, *que voulez-vous?*' she remarked. 'The best of both worlds.'

'And a name like L'Amour?' I queried.

'Splendid! I can just imagine myself saying, "L'Amour, please give me another—" '

'Look here,' I cut in, 'I am merely trying to fix up a goalkeeper.'

In due course L'Amour arrived in the village, escorted by 'Sailor' Thompsett. He was tall, lithe, dark and, as 'Sailor' had said, quite handsome. Indeed, his name fitted him like a sheath; he positively exuded *l'amour* and *galanterie*. I don't think he normally behaved like this in his own country, but he wanted to create a good impression. He won over Flossie by kissing her hand, though the *habituées* of the Hole were dubitative of him. He soon became the centre of attraction for Bill Blurge's Lill, not to mention some others of the United's camp followers, as Clive Harrison-Tracey called them. There were the usual, polite, stilted phrases in English: 'I am so 'appy to be in your so lovely English village' . . . '*Enchanté, mam'selle*, I am - how do you say? – up the pole to meet you.'

'He'll be up the flippin' pole before I've finished with him,' darkly added Bill Blurge. 'Wot the flippin' hell does "Sailor" think ee's playin' at? I reckon as 'ow 'ee wants to bust the flippin' team wide open bringing a Froggie with 'is fancy ways down 'ere.'

After a long session at the Hole, during which L'Amour (his Christian name was François) declined to drink anything other than orange juice – to the disgust of the others – we all went down to the Devil's Frying Pan. It was Bill Blurge's suggestion that 'we try this Froggie out between the sticks'. I think the name of the village football ground frightened François L'Amour, for he kept repeating it to himself in an awed and disbelieving voice. In fact, the 'Pan' was a natural setting for football. The bowl of the 'frying pan' sloped gently to the pitch, providing

Nature's own terracing, and the long, narrow 'handle' was a perfect approach and parking place for cars and coaches. Not that Codiham's matches presented a car-parking problem.

L'Amour soon silenced the critics at that evening's practice with a quite remarkable display of acrobatics between the goalposts. Of course, he had the continental's love of showing off. He couldn't resist a spectacular somersault even in saving a fairly easy shot, but some of his tips over the bar from point-blank range, his swift pounces to cut out centres from the wings were superbly timed and executed. He was certainly the best goalkeeper Codiham had ever seen.

His interview with Mr. Pargetter was unexpectedly successful. It transpired that L'Amour had worked for a French hotelier whom Mrs. Pargetter knew quite well. Thus it was that François L'Amour became barman in the lobby bar, despite much head-shaking by Young George. However, as Young George was a staunch Codiham United supporter, he couldn't say very much about it.

L'Amour played in the first match of the season. He saved a penalty shot and thus gained a precious point for the United. But, with the autumn of that year developing into a belated heat-wave, the Green was given over to 'cucking' with a feverish abandon into which François soon found himself drawn willy-nilly. What with working at the Merry Damsel, football and philandering, he was kept abnormally busy.

In his favour it could be said that the more forward of the village maidens never gave him a chance. And, of course, he couldn't help his name. To his slight disadvantage it must be admitted that he was a born philanderer; he just could not help 'making frens weeth zeese rosy-cheeked girls of zee Engleesh countryside'. Yet François was not a lecher, nor did he seek to disrupt other people's friendships: 'I unnerstan eet ees – 'ow do you say? – not done to take zee *petite amie* of a team-mate,' he told me. 'Zees Lill, she make life vairy deefecult. I must explain to Beel Blurge zat I do not weesh to make 'er march weeth me.'

One thing Mr. Pargetter frankly discouraged at the outset was the visit to the lobby bar of the Merry Damsel by L'Amour's new-found girl friends. When he found them popping in for shandy gaffs and ginger beers so that they could sit and make sheep's eyes at François, he resolved that this was one French Revolution with which he was not in accord. This happened two nights running, much to the disapproval of the bar's regular customers. Then Pargetter struck: calling François aside, he told him to take over in the dining-room while he presided in the bar.

Mr. Pargetter could be the most charming of hosts, but, when he wanted (which, fortunately, was rare), he could be disapprovingly forbidding. For a week he appeared in the bar at opening time and the girls, quite unused to the lobby bar of the Merry Damsel and somewhat abashed by the frigid looks of the 'regulars', soon gave up calling in.

This did not deter them from pursuit of François. At closing time there were usually three or four of them waiting under the beeches outside the Merry Damsel just for the pleasure of walking across the Green with the barman. And it cannot be said that François had the excuse of going to his lodgings, for he had been installed in the Priest's Hole and his purpose in taking a walk across the Green can hardly have been that he was in need of air.

Foolish was François, but he couldn't help it. He got himself hopelessly entangled. When he was walking across the Green with Meg, Phyllis and Maisie, he was always scheming how to get Meg to himself. As Meg lived at the far end of the village and he saw her home last, this wasn't very difficult until Phyllis astutely diagnosed the subterfuge. Then, as a compromise, he agreed to spend his afternoons off with Phyllis. This arrangement worked fairly well until Maisie asked him to sneak up to her kitchen window at 1 a.m. three nights a week. Maisie lived with her widower father who went on shift work on these three nights of the week, so Maisie, who was always in the habit of giving her father a cup of tea before he set forth, lured François with a similar prospect about ten minutes after Papa had left the house.

'I do not know 'ow I shall play football, eef zees goes on,' François told me sadly. 'This gay life in Codgem eet ees too much for me. First I am with Meg, then Maisie – she no like being alone in ze 'ouse when her father goes to work – and then in ze afternoon when I meet Phyllis, I am – 'ow do you say? – too sleepy for zee love-making.'

7. Eva tackles the jungle

As has already been said, we were not gardeners, nor was this a modest fiction on our part. The stark, awful truth was that we not only knew nothing of the theory of gardening, but were in almost total ignorance of the names of most of the trees, flowers, plants and weeds which grew around the oast.

Many strange and unlovely things were flourishing in the half-acre which surrounded us (not to mention the hidden quarter-acre which we discovered later), and, if we learned nothing else during those early weeks, we certainly extended our knowledge of weeds. We had every facility for studying them in the greatest detail and I must say in the light of experience that, for anyone trying to create a garden out of nothing, it is far more important to know your weeds than the names of your roses.

Perhaps one day I shall write a textbook on weeds. It is a job that needs to be done and would be far more valuable to the amateur gardener than treatises on 'How to build a lily pond', or 'The art of growing dahlias.'

Mind you, I don't say that the importance of weeds dawned on us as swiftly as all that. Nor did we fully realize at first that a permanent state of military preparedness is necessary to counteract pests. We jollied along as simple appeasers of all things crawling in the foolish belief that sufficient unto the day was the weevil thereof. Our first reaction to the fact that the environment of the Oast House contained a jungle of charlock, sow-thistle, chowclay, nettles, dandelions, bindweed, broom and rotting black currant bushes was to pretend airily, even to ourselves, that there wasn't a garden problem.

We would say: 'Oh, well, it's only half an acre,' knowing perfectly well we should have preferred a tiny stone courtyard in which we could lazily arrange a few painted tubs of hydrangeas, seat ourselves in deck-chairs and complacently call it a day. If such escapism failed always to assuage our horticultural conscience, we would dismiss the matter by arguing that autumn was coming and it was too late to do anything about it before next spring.

But others did not permit us to forget things quite so easily. Whenever Dick Pride left the Oast, he would shake his head and point knowingly at the weedy jungle, saying: 'You've got a proper job on there.' The postman unfailingly scratched his head and repeated morning after morning: 'Glad it's you and not me as 'as to put that to rights.' Not exactly a cheerful reminder that another day had dawned even for people like ourselves who still regarded the country as a Great Adventure. And, as the days shortened and the leaves began to fall, other visitors would take up this cry like the chorus of a Greek tragedy, more sorrowfully than inquisitively. No one was rude enough to ask when we proposed to start doing anything about it; all assumed that any moment we were about to get cracking.

Being a natural optimist, I kept telling myself that one day some kindly labourer would peer over the brick wall that separated us from Cucking Green and offer to tackle the job for us. Instead some extrovert lout who had just left the public bar of the Bearpits would lean over the wall and cry: 'Mister, wot you want here is a gaggle of they convicts from Dartmoor,' and then stagger off with throaty chuckles. We didn't exactly see the funny side of it.

Soon we found ourselves mumbling excuses about 'getting the house straight first', which, in a way, was true. Ultimately it dawned on us that something would have to be done – quickly.

The 'jungle' – I refuse to pretend it was anything else at the time – was an awkwardly-shaped monstrosity of a plot, a hideous child of Nature at her worst and man in his most bloody-minded mood. It was Anthony who christened it the 'jungle' and for him it was a vast continent waiting to be explored, a hunting-ground for Red Indians, or a setting for enacting the doughtiest deeds of Davy Crockett, according to his personal programme for the day. In his lively imagination the 'jungle' was invested with a glamour that enabled him to regard weeds as palm trees, which, indeed, they threatened to rival in height.

At the front of the Oast there was a shambles of 70 per cent weed, 20 per cent rubble, 8 per cent clover and 2 per cent grass. This was a more or less square plot which could be tamed. It was at the sides and back of the Oast where the problem became acute. There was a winding strip of land, starting from a clump of firs on the churchyard boundary, only about 20 yards narrow to begin with, but gradually increasing in width until it descended sharply into a hollow which must have been used as a refuse dump for the past century. When I first saw the hollow it was roughly fenced off by some rusty barbed wire and I foolishly imagined that it had nothing to do with us. It was only after we had acquired the property and studied the plans that we realized that this quarter-acre hollow was ours. My first thought was to try to sell it. But who would buy a refuse dump?

The hollow was a grotesque, putrescent blister on the property; it was so full of rubbish, rotten timber, old tins, bricks, decaying boots and weeds that it was practically impenetrable. If one approached within 10 yards of it the stink was such that only a Gaulloise cigarette, furiously puffed and exhaled, could enable one to survive the ordeal. To enter the hollow was to invite even worse fates, for the whole area was mined with wasps' nests and infested by a colony of rats. There were also clearly defined rat-runs right along the narrow strip.

As you will see, there were very few assets in this jungle. Indeed, at first, when we came to inspect the territory rather more thoroughly, we were so immersed in gloom that we could not appreciate even these few. Later it dawned on us that some things were worth salving. Being methodical for once, we made a list of these. It read as follows:

(1) Clump of firs: pleasant to look at and useful in hiding the view of the tombstones in Saint Mildred's Churchyard.

(2) Two hedges forming the boundaries at the back of the property, one of lilac and the other of blackberries. (The lilac reminded my wife of Ivor Novello and the blackberries would make an excellent pie.)

(3) Broom clumps. We disagreed on this subject, but I pointed out that (a) they would save money which might otherwise be spent on rhododendrons and (b) they provided a marvellous splash of colour in their relatively short season.

(4) About eighteen trees which we listed as (a) cooking apple, (b) cherry, (c) plum and (d) unknown. Item (d) was later identified as two maple trees.

(5) Various strange flowers which appeared inconsequentially among the weeds and which 'might come in useful if transplanted'.

(6) All grass and clover which might ultimately be separated from its faster-breeding, weedy companions.

I have only two pieces of advice worth passing on to other Town clots who may be rash enough to make a garden. At the risk of being a bore (and on the earnest promise that I shall not attempt any further advice in later chapters) I will pass these on to you. The first is that you should on no account try to find the roots of such weeds as bind-weed and thistle; if you do, you will find that the quest – like that for the rainbow – never ends. You will either tunnel your way underneath your home and probably disturb the foundations, or cause such surface havoc to your prospective garden that only a combination of tractor and excavator will put it right. Much better to pay somebody to bring along a tractor at the start. Most of the weeds will still pop up again the following year anyhow, but you will at least have been saved the mental strain of pulling at roots which seem as long and as tough as a cruiser's hawsers. And don't expect to get your weeds under control for at least four years.

This, I admit, is negative advice, but it will save a great deal of anguish, heartache, slipped discs and lumbago, not to mention domestic strife. More important, however, is Point Number Two. This concerns the sixth item on our list of things to be salved.

All gardening books I have read invariably assume that you prefer to make a lawn the hard way. You are told when to clear the ground, how to dig it, how to rake it over and, finally, how, when and where to sow the precious, expensive grass seeds, or reverently to set down the sods – what an appropriate word! – of Cumberland turf. Unless you are planning to create a Wembley football pitch, or a miniature Lords, this professional gardening tarradiddle is the most absolute tushery ever blithely accepted by amateur gardeners.

Revolt against such advice unless you wish to fill the pockets of the grass-seed firms and the spivs who sell you dead sods of inferior grass and pretend it's Cumberland turf. Unless you are prepared to live like a pauper for a few years, to forego a new car, not to mention the next two annual holidays, to follow this advice when creating a lawn of half an acre upwards is like meekly accepting a sentence of hard labour and bread-and-water diet. If you think I exaggerate and reply that thousands of men do it and show no signs of regret, I shall still be unimpressed. Either they have unlimited purses and are prepared to pay somebody to do the job for them, or they are the crassest idiots I have ever come across.

I am paying you the honour of assuming that you neither have a bottomless purse, nor are you a crass idiot. What you should do first is to make sure you have a reasonably level stretch of land. It need not matter if there are slight slopes, or a few dips in the middle, but never make a lawn on a bank, or anything approaching a hill. The true test of this is to picture whether you would like to push a mower up a steep bank.

Having decided that you have a passably level stretch of land, tear up, or preferably burn the larger and more easily managed weeds. In fact, have several bonfires going at once and don't worry about the fact that it will make the ground look like a battlefield. In doing all this take care to retain any patch of grass or clover that still remains after weeding. If such patches still contain a proportion of weed, don't let that worry you. It is better to have a few weeds than to destroy what grass and clover there is in the process.

You may not think so, but you are now practically finished in your work. But everybody will tell you the contrary. You will be told you should have dug up everything and then rolled it and raked it over. You must resist such advice and reply that you have filled up two hollows with earth from one mound and done five minutes' rolling in one corner and that, as far as you are concerned, you now propose to sit back and see what happens.

You will be called a stubborn moron, a crazy coot and many other epithets, but you must still Stand Firm. Seed firms will bombard you with catalogues; even if you haven't written for them, somebody else in a 'do-good' mood will secretly urge them to lure you with photographs of lawns like the proverbial billiard table.

If you continue to refuse to buy any grass seed at all, if you remain stubborn and sit back until the spring, your efforts will be rewarded. Slowly the tiny patches of grass and clover will fan out and fill up the vast open spaces of earth. True, weeds will reappear as well, but, by mowing and rolling (and not too much rolling, remember), even the weeds will slowly disappear again and, by the end of the first summer, you will have a reasonably level patch of grass and clover. In two years you will be able to call it a lawn, though other people may still scoff at the idea. Within three to five years even the scoffers will pay you the tribute of saying, 'We would never have believed it.' And, if you keep on mowing and rolling for twenty years and your son and grandson carry on the good work after that, it will become a lawn in under a

century. Technically a lawn that is; from your own point of view it will
have been a lawn after the second year.

This is a lazy man's idea of creating a lawn, but I can assure you it
does work. Which is more than you can say about many lawns sown
from seed. As a rash concession to the experts I once sowed some grass
seed in one of the larger empty patches around the Oast. Out of these
expensive, twelve-shillings-a-pound seeds grew a vast area of Shepherd's
Purse that compared most unfavourably with my self-seeding clover-
and-grass patch alongside it. The result of my methods is a tremendous
saving in cash, personal effort and labour costs, plus the intense
satisfaction that accrues from anything achieved with the minimum of
work.

But, chronologically, I am speaking out of turn. There was no intense
satisfaction in mid-September when we shrank from the prospect of
having any physical contact with so immense a problem as taming the
jungle. All we did was to write to three landscape gardeners, asking for
estimates. Our idea was to hand over the whole question to them, sit
back and await results. Meanwhile, we congratulated ourselves that there
was no hedge to be clipped in front of the Oast and that the red-brick
wall which separated us from Cucking Green had stood the test of time.
We removed the broken-down wooden stile which had previously been
the sole entrance to our new home and Dick Pride had set in its place a
second-hand, wrought-iron gate which was not only elegant, but
permitted us to look at the pond.

Needless to say the landscape gardeners seemed to imagine we wanted
to turn our wilderness into a cross between Kew Gardens and the more
ornate parts of Blenheim Palace's exquisite grounds. I won't go into
details, but the grand total of all three of their estimates came to more
than £1,000. We should have had to sell the Oast House at a handsome
profit to save ourselves from bankruptcy if we had accepted any one of
their designs. Each firm seemed bent on giving us a garden that would
take all day and night to look after, with floodlit, sunken rose-beds,
mis-shapen gnomes and grotesquely large stone rabbits, rockeries that
would require mountaineering qualifications, if one were to attempt to
keep them in order, and a pond for goldfish that would need cleaning out
once a year.

Never, however, in our moments of deepest despair did we contem-
plate 'going it alone'. Town clots we might be, but not such clots as to
imagine we could pit our ignorance against Nature. And, as Sylvia
rightly pointed out, we didn't come to the country to become slaves to

it. So, as in most crises, we turned to that Admiral Crichton of Codiham, 'Sailor' Thompsett.

'A gardener?' said an aghast 'Sailor' with the incredulity one might expect if he had been asked to book us a passage to the moon. 'There ain't such folk around today except for one or two old uns who can hardly move for arthritis. There are jobbers, but more'n likely they're potterers than aught else. You won't find many young uns who ull tackle a job like yourn. Why it's like asking someone to start digging up a tropical jungle. Still, I'll see what I can do. There's just one chance.'

'The 'one chance' turned out to be a rumbustious and heftily-built lass named Eva, a close-cropped, mousy-haired Amazon of a woman with thighs like a man's and buttocks like prize pumpkins. Eva had served as a Land Girl in the Second World War. She was Codiham-born-and-bred, loved 'just pottering about' and did jobbing-gardening by day and was a member of the Bearpits' darts team by night. She drank pints of bitter like a man, threw a nifty dart and was generally regarded as 'a bit mad, but a good sport'.

When first introduced to her by 'Sailor' in the Bearpits I was frankly alarmed by this formidable character. No one would have said Eva was handsome; on the other hand it would be inaccurate to say she was ugly. She had a freckled, polished oak-hued face and large brown eyes, which were her best feature. Her manner was masculine, forthright and, on first impressions, truculent. But the truculence was really a mask. If Eva had been born in Cucking Manor instead of in a cottage at Henty, she would have been a hard-riding, hard-drinking, hard-swearing huntswoman, putting the fear of God into every man in the district. As it was her darts team colleagues were a bit scared of her and secretly jealous because she had beaten them in a contest for drinking a yard of ale in the quickest time. My only fear was whether we could hold our own with such a tough customer. But there was little choice: 'Sailor' had indicated pretty clearly that it was Eva, or nothing.

'I'll come an' give yer place a look over,' she told me. 'Drop in tomorrow morning, if that suits you. 'arf a crown an hour I charge an' me lunch thrown in if I puts in a full day's work. Beer, cheese and pickles, that's me midday cheer-me-up.'

'Sailor' took me on one side afterwards. 'Eva's a good worker, none better,' he said. 'She's cheap at 'arf a crown an hour. There's just one thing I should warn you of?'

'Oh, and what's that? I suppose she drinks.'

'No, not that. Eva drinks plenty, but she can 'old it better'n most. No, Eva has one weakness. She's a proper menace in the round house.'

'The round house?'

'The lavatory, sir. Lor' bless you, our Eva 'as a passion for lavatories. It don't matter whether they are round 'ouses, which is wot I, as a sea-farin' man, calls ladies' and gentlemen's lavatories, or the old lemon-squeezer like they 'ave at the Hole in the Wall. Eva can't keep out of 'em.'

'You mean her bladder is weak?'

'Sailor' hooted. 'Not that it ain't. No, Eva is a bit of a wit in her way. A poet, I suppose you could say. But she gets her inspiration in lavatories. She don't sit down and write 'er poems, she scrawls 'em on the walls.'

'Extraordinary. You mean she might do the same at the Oast House?'

'Well, that's the risk. She's as honest as they go, she wouldn't steal a penny. You could leave yer silver lying around and Eva ud never touch un. But let 'er get in yer round 'ouse, well, she couldn't resist leaving 'er mark. She got the sack from old Miss Ablethorpe at The Limes for doing just that.'

'But what sort of poems are they?' I inquired, with visions of bawdy verse appearing on our lavatory walls.

'Oh, they're proper saucy,' said 'Sailor' with a wicked grin. 'You'd better keep an eye on her.'

.   .   .   .   .

With the problem of the jungle looming larger every day, I think we should have settled for almost anyone to 'do' the garden. I personally was quite prepared to risk occasional verses appearing on the lavatory walls, if Eva would agree to clear up the wilderness of bindweed and chickweed and remove the tufts of thistle and nettle. But I hardly thought it tactful to tell my wife about Eva's little hobby.

Eva arrived punctually to pass her judgement. Hands on hips, legs well apart, cigarette between her lips, she pronounced it: 'Could be worse. But that 'ollow is a proper Rattlesnake Creek. Can't touch that till we get rid of they wopses' nests and the rats.'

It was Jim Brickness, Codiham United's left-back and the village grave-digger, who dealt with the wasps' nests and the rats. Jim was secretary of the Codiham Rat and Sparrow Club, which had its head-quarters at the Bearpits. I never quite knew whether the club existed primarily for the extermination of vermin, or for the annual dinner at which a cup is presented to the member with the greatest record of slaughter over the year. But there is no doubt that, whatever the motives of its members, the annual campaign produced remarkable results. In 1958 Jim Bricknell himself killed 107 queen wasps, 31 grey squirrels and 247 rats.

While Jim was coping with the rats and wasps, Eva proceeded to arm herself with a formidable battery of implements to tackle the jungle. I had given her *carte blanche* to get whatever she thought was necessary and she certainly returned with what looked like the contents of an entire ironmonger's shop, wheeling up to the house a barrow containing spades, scythes, secateurs, pitchfork, shears, old sacks, balls of string, a rake, a saw and what looked like a butcher's shop.

'Surely,' I exclaimed in amazement, 'you won't want that much just for this?'

I instantly regretted the remark. 'Humph,' replied Eva, 'this lot could do with a couple of tanks and a flame-thrower as well. You wait and see.'

Muttering curses to herself, Eva wielded the scythes – first one, then the other – with a skill and ferocity that alarmed us both. 'She will cut her legs off, if she isn't careful,' commented Sylvia. 'I don't know much about scything, but it seems an odd way of going about it to me.'

It was. But that was Eva – unorthodox, doing everything in an odd manner, yet getting results; fast-working, individualistic and happy-go-lucky. When the front plot was scythed down it was soon apparent that it was not as flat as we had been led to believe. Weed is a great leveller, but underneath it all was a bumpy surface of grassy mounds and brick-bottomed hollows. It was then that we made the most appalling discovery of all: the square plot was a mere two inches of soil covering what had been the brick yard of the Oast.

So each brick had to be dug out until we had a pile of them about six feet high in one corner of the – well, what was to be the garden. This task was completed by early October. During the whole time she had been with us Eva had never once shown any inclination to visit either of our two lavatories. Now, standing back to survey the pile of bricks, she ventured: 'Tell you wot, sir, them bricks ud come in nice and handy to make a liddle lavender in the hollow.'

'Lavender?' I queried. 'How can you make lavender with bricks?'

Eva laughed. 'Ah, sir, I see you doan't know all our Codgem sayings yet. A "lavender" is an outside closet. I sees you ain't got one.'

Here we go, I thought. At last the real Eva is revealing herself. Until then I had suspected that 'Sailor' Thompsett had been pulling my leg.

'Oh, I don't know,' I replied. 'I don't think we really need one.'

'Um, pity. I likes to see a nice lavender in the garden. Saves a lot of journeys upstairs, I says.'

'You know, Eva, we have two – er – lavenders already, downstairs and up.'

'Oh, they're not proper lavenders unless they're outside. I doan't like indoors ones. Not private, they ain't. All these noisy chains making a clatter and water gurgling in the pipes. Draws attention like to wot you's doin'.'

Nothing more was said at the time and the bricks were set aside for a vague project I had about a sunken garden and a lily pond at some future date. Meanwhile, Eva won our hearts by her good nature and her immense efforts to tame a semblance of order out of the Poesque chaos which had hitherto existed. It could have been gardening with tears for an amateur at the Oast House. With Eva it was gardening with belly laughs, with gay abandon, carelessness, if you like, but progress never-theless, and never a murmur of complaint. Occasionally I erred as all amateurs will err in autumn when they try their hand at transplanting. The forced bulbs I had put in the ground came up unexpectedly looking like some obscene fungi imported from outer space. Eva's blunt comment summed up my errors neatly: 'You stuck 'em in too deep, you brought 'em out too soon. That's allus the trouble with the men whether it's with women or gardening.'

True, she lost things. The secateurs which she 'left for 'arf a mo' in late September turned up in a wild rhubarb bed early in November. But she was never still, always questing for something to do, probing our unmade-up minds for views on how to develop the garden. But to plan a garden in November is like having to think about the next summer's holiday at Christmas – an unmitigated bore. All we wanted Eva to do was to carry on with her admirable mopping-up operations. This she did with enthusiasm and I noted that, next to lavatories, her passion seemed to be for bonfires. 'I wish every night were Bonfire Night,' she would say, a sentiment which was heartily echoed by my son for whom she made the most magnificent Guy Fawkes on the 5th of November, creating an effigy of a stockbroker farmer of the district for whom she had a demoniac hatred. Just to make sure the effigy should be recognized she attached a large label with his name on it. Throughout November and December she was starting bonfires, lighting them, cosseting them, cursing them, rekindling them and encouraging them to billow out huge clouds of suffocating, blue smoke that made the precincts of the Oast rather like a battlefield on the Somme.

.   .   .   .   .

Our downstairs 'loo' was sandwiched between the front door and a cupboard in which cleaning materials and divers domestic appliances were kept. And it is perfectly true that a casual visitor wishing to enter the 'loo' needed to be carefully directed. He could so easily either disappear outside the front-door, or find himself in the cupboard: the three doors – from the interior of the house at least – were exactly alike.

Eva had been told where the 'loo' was, but – or so we thought – she had never used it. Once, when she returned from paying a call of nature at the Bearpits down the road (a tedious journey for so simple a purpose), Sylvia had pointed out to her that her trip was hardly necessary. 'Oh,' replied Eva, 'I allus gets the cupboard and that other place mixed up.'

There seemed a note of contempt in her reference to 'that other place', as though the fact that we lacked a 'lavender' still rankled.

But one day Eva did use our 'loo'. She also left her unmistakable signature. When she had gone we found chalked up on the top left-hand corner of the door, facing the hall, the cryptic phrase 'YERTIS'.

'What on earth does she mean?' asked a puzzled Sylvia.

'I gather the general idea is to let people know that here it is – YERTIS.'

'Here is what?'

'Why, the loo of course.'

'But we know it is.'

'Ah, but Eva can never remember.'

'But surely she must know you can't go around writing on other people's doors? I mean, she must be mad, quite mad. I wonder—'

Sylvia made a move to open the door. I intervened.

'No, not yet,' I added firmly. 'I think I'd better look first.'

'You don't think—'

I don't know what Sylvia thought, or what she expected I would find inside the 'loo', but I had a pretty good hunch that Eva had been up to something more than chalking on the outside. I hadn't read my Freud for nothing.

She had, but, bless her simple heart, Eva had not committed the unforgivable sin of writing on the walls. She must have been sorely tempted for days, perhaps weeks, but, resisting the temptation, had gone home to ponder over the best solution for her difficulty. And inside the 'loo' she had hung up a framed piece of her own verse, etched with a burnt cork on one of those rough and tough pieces of brown paper you find in railway toilets. It read:

> North, south, east, west,
> A rose is sweet, but lavender's best.
> Since you call this place a loo,
> I must say it has a lovely view.

Indeed, it had, for through the tiny window opposite the seat was an uninterrupted vision of the pond and the swans, the cricket pitch and the Merry Damsel in the distance. Of course, I had to explain to Sylvia about Eva's passion for versifying in lavatories and the warning 'Sailor' Thompsett had given me. I was relieved to find that Eva had paid us the compliment of reserving her bawdier verse for the 'lavenders' of Codiham.

'But what are we to do about it?' Sylvia asked. 'If we say nothing, we may offend her. After all it is framed, and I suppose the words are, well, quite nicely meant. But if we thank her, she may take it as a hint to go on with her handiwork. Next time she may set about the upstairs "loo" and heaven knows what inspiration she may draw from those framed prints of Toulouse-Lautrec's naughtier pictures.'

'It's pretty indifferent verse,' I said, 'otherwise we might leave it up there.'

'There's no need to be a snob,' chided Sylvia, always ready to defend other women from man's barbs. 'It rhymes, which is more than you can say for some people's verse. I say we should leave it up there and hope our visitors take it as a good joke.'

'It will take quite a bit of explaining,' I replied. 'It isn't particularly funny to anyone but us. The whole point of it is in knowing about Eva's little weakness.'

'Really, darling, you're quite exasperating. You talk as though she had a weak bladder, or something.'

'I happen to know she hasn't. Anyhow, I agree with you, we had best leave it there. The "YERTIS" notice *is* quite useful.'

In the end we compromised. The 'YERTIS' message was allowed to stay on the door. The framed verse was constantly being taken down and put up again, depending on the type of visitor we had. We tossed up as to who should speak to Eva on the subject and I lost. I thanked her for her kindly thought in putting up the framed verse and said what a splendid idea it was to put the notice on the door. But, I added, all people wouldn't appreciate Eva's undoubted talent; there were narrow-minded folk who might – well, take a dim view of the affair. We couldn't risk having other similar works of art around the house.

'Oh, I allus keeps my thoughts to the lavenders and privys. Some folks ain't got no sense of 'umour,' snorted Eva. 'But I allus says there's real democracy in the lavender. Wot you says there applies to all folks. Mind you, sir, I was proper careful wot I put in your "loo" – never 'eard that name for it afore – but I won't say as 'ow I ain't bin tempted by some naughty thoughts when I was in the ladies' at the Bearpits. I started my verse there – my very first effort. But you ought to see the walls now. Once you start writin' poetry, it's like measles, it's catchin'. Every lass in this village must 'ave added her own little ditty. Oh, yes, us be a proper wicked lot of girls down at Codgem when it comes to makin' up verses.'

I don't think Eva was below average intelligence. In her own way she knew when to draw the line and she certainly attempted no more verse on our walls. I once asked her if she had read much poetry and she answered meaningly, 'No, but I've 'eard an awful lot. Miss Able-thorpe used to recite liddle gardening verses and that "Sailor" Thompsett knows some corkers.' And her wink conveyed the fact that she much preferred the bawdier limericks to Miss Ablethorpe's gardening-by-rhyme homilies.

I have not, of course, been able to inspect Eva's handiwork in the ladies' 'loo' at the Bearpits, though the landlord has assured me that 'it's blue, but not libellous'.

.   .   .   .   .

By the end of the year the jungle had been tamed and, sitting by the fire in the oast room, we were able to draw some rough sketches of what the garden ought to look like. I was pleased to note that one or two small patches of grass still existed on the front square which we ultimately intended to be a lawn. I was somewhat disturbed, knowing Eva's obsession with lavatories, to hear her say one day that she was going to 'besom all over your lawn'. Nice as it was to know that Eva (though no one else as yet) referred to 'it' as a 'lawn', I really began to wonder whether 'besom', like 'lavender', wasn't a Sussex word for something slightly indelicate, though no doubt of pressing importance.

However, I soon learned that to 'besom' was to brush, just as 'to brush the hedges' was to cut them. Sylvia was the first to be caught out on the latter piece of rural fantasy; she even went to fetch Eva a tough-bristled hand-brush and inquired whether that would be 'all right'. 'They'd whisk me off to Hellingly if they saw me using that on the hedges,' was Eva's bosom-heaving, buttock-shaking, gusty-laughtered response to this offer.

But soon we got used to such gardener's lore. We began to recognize when something was 'making wood', or when a rose tree had 'gone home'. Not that we intended to become preoccupied with such temperamental, 'easy to get took sick' (Eva's description) things as roses. They were, added Eva, 'a bloomin' worry all the year round and wot with the pruning and the grafting and the spraying and then all the dried blood for feedin' 'em up, they ain't worth the bloody candle'.

Eva herself 'hadn't much time for flowers'. She would have liked us to turn most of the half-acre into a kitchen garden, but I argued that for a family of three it was quite ridiculous to have more vegetables than we could possibly eat at a time when they were at their cheapest in the shops and, conversely, none at all when they were at their most expensive. However, Eva persuaded us to 'go careful like' on roses. She was quite right; they are lovely, but fundamentally delinquent in character.

By January our nearest approach to gardening was with paper and pencil, assisted by rulers and flower-charts, in front of crackling logs and inspired by mulled rum and ale. Eva always took her 'annual' at the end of January; it consisted of a prolonged visit to a sister who ran a tea-shop in Lewes. I rather suspect, though I can't imagine it, that Eva earned some beer money by acting as a washer-up. I always have promised myself a visit to that tea-shop just to inspect the 'loo'.

8. *Night life in the village*

IT is a great mistake to think that a village is devoid of night life. Indeed, the chief charm of the best sort of village is that it guards its night life as a precious thing only to be shared by a few. True, you may go to a village and suspect that after closing time at the local pub the blinds are drawn and the shutters put up and all is silence until the first milkman appears about dawn. But that is because villagers keep their night life to themselves and away from the pryings of inquisitive 'furriners'.

Never once during the first few months of our existence in Codiham did it penetrate our town skulls that the village boasted of any other form of night life than 'cucking' on the Green. But gradually one received veiled hints, often the merest sly whisper of 'goings on' in the hours of darkness. The password for obtaining such information seemed to be 'adry', a meaningful Sussex phrase that conveys not so much a desire to have a common thirst quenched, as a lustful, zestful passion for more liquid at a late hour and any other pleasures that might suitably accompany such indulgence.

'He be proper adry tonight,' I would sometimes hear Young George say in the snug of the Merry Damsel. 'I reckon 'ee'l find 'is way to Ma Kittle's bough house.'

Ma Kittle's bough house was a hang-over from a ruder age. A century ago certain private houses in Sussex were allowed to sell liquor during fairs. A bush on the end of a pole in a cottage garden was the badge of such a bough house. Hence the phrase: 'Good wine needs no bush', which was really meant to cast doubts on the quality of bough-house liquor. Ma Kittle had no such permission to sell strong drink and it is certain that the licensing justices would have turned down any application she might make. But, as Young George said, 'in 'er Grandpa's time 't were a bough house and a bough house 't will allus be for us villagers.'

This bough house was situated at the end of Bearpits Lane, a some-what tumble-down thatched dwelling rejoicing in the name of Howler's Cottage. Though she displayed no bush on a pole in her minute garden, Ma Kittle was never known to turn anyone away who 'wanted a bit of fun of a night'. As to what constituted 'a bit of fun', few would admit any details, or definition, but there was talk of bumboo juice and a cosy little back parlour where, doubtless among the aspidistras and potted ferns, on a wet winter's night 'a cucker can take his lass. Or happen, if 'ee ain't got no lass, Ma Kittle ul find un one,' said Young George with a wicked grin. 'Oh, yes, she's the lonely virgin's friend is Ma Kittle, and many as ain't no virgins neither.'

Whenever I expressed enthusiasm for initiation into the mysterious rite of Ma Kittle's 'bumboo nights', I was merely told 'it were only for the few.' Bumboo[1] is apparently a compound of diverse spirituous liquors which is only brewed in a few homes belonging to the Howlers' Fratern-ity. The Howlers – and doubtless Ma Kittle's cottage got its name from these folk – used to be youths who went wassailing in the orchards on the eve of Epiphany, but today there are only a few of them left. You can tell which is the home of a Howler when you see a red lantern placed in a window on Epiphany Eve. This is the signal that from midnight onwards bumboo will be served to all Howlers and womenfolk who work in the orchards. A bawdy and uproarious night is then enjoyed by all. 'Bumboo do do things to 'ee,' says Young George. 'Once drunk 'tis never forgotten and it's as good for making a lass in the mood for a gambol as anything drunk in the whole of Sussex. Mind 'ee, if a girl once gets a taste for the stuff, yer ull 'ave nothing but trouble with un. But for the man it works wonders and fair puts lead in yer pencil. There were old Jacket in Silk Lane who never 'ad luck with 'ooman. Married three times 'ee were, and thrice divorced or nullified. When it came to

[1] I regret I have not discovered the recipe for bumboo, but its existence is confirmed by the Rev. W. D. Parish, who quotes from the 1756 diary of an East Hoathly draper: 'I went down to Jones' where we drank one bowl of punch and two muggs of bumboo, and I came home again in liquor. Oh, with what horrors does it fill my heart to think I should be found guilty of doing this!'

marriage he bain't got green fingers, or summat. Then one night 'ee went to Ma Kittle's bough house and since 'ee's never looked back. Married to a young girl of eighteen wot he brought to bed in Ma Kittle's back parlour, all on bumboo juice, too.'

Yet the first real hint of nocturnal activities came, oddly enough, from our soberest and earliest visitor to the Oast House, Harry Sprogget, of the village store. Harry had one son and four daughters, but he stubbornly ignored the fact that his daughters all served in the shop at some time or another and called his business 'Sprogget & Sons, Grocers Extraordinary'. When I pointed out this discrepancy to him, he studiously avoided any acknowledgement of his daughters' existence, but added that he believed there was 'another young Sprogget on the way and it's sure to be a grandson.'

Superficially 'Grocers Extraordinary' seemed a ridiculously grandiloquent title for what was a village store. But, if you penetrated through the maze of brooms, pots and pans, sides of bacon, jars of jam, and baskets of eggs and fruit which caused acute congestion in his shop, it was possible to find a bulging Ali Baba's cave of unexpected delicacies and gourmet's delights in the darkest corners. It was, in fact (and still is, I am glad to say) an eternal pleasure to enter Sprogget's.

Harry was practically our first caller after the man from the Water Company had turned on the taps. Armed with a bulky note-book and a red pencil, he came to see what he might 'do us' for. It sounded ominous, but Harry was helpfulness itself. We had just moved in, hadn't we? Ah, yes, the solicitor's clerk at Mortiboy and Fawcett had told him. And, of course, we should be wanting to 'stock up'. Now he always believed that everybody had their own 'special tastes . . . some likes streaky and some likes lots of lean. And, naturally, coming from Lunnon, doubtless you have some very original ideas of what to eat.'

'One would think we were cannibals,' said Sylvia. 'What on earth does he think we eat?'

Harry Sprogget was not slow in making suggestions. A very fine line in turtle soup, just the thing for Christmas, with a drop of cooking sherry in it. Or, come to think of it, with a name like McCormick, what about some haggis? Yes, he had tinned haggis all right – stocked it ever since the vet. came to the village. Oh, yes, he was a Scot, too. Had he any Gruyère cheese? Well, no (somewhat sadly), that was one of the cheeses with which he hadn't 'made an acquaintance. But I can get it for you. Oh, yes, I can get anything.'

And, indeed, he could. In this fashion for something like thirty years

Harry had built up a thriving business. It was based on his own bustling, non-stop salesmanship at the doors of every newcomer to Codiham and the fact that, if he hadn't anything you asked for, he promptly said: 'Never worry, madam, I'll rectify it.' The rectifications were innumerable over the years with the result that his village store did earn the title of 'extraordinary'. Because Miss Ablethorpe had acquired a passion for rose-petal jam following a trip to Morocco, Harry stocked it. Colonel Skinner still liked to imagine himself back in Aurungabad in the days when George Nathaniel Curzon lorded it over the Raj and, as a sacrificial tribute to this former pig-sticker, Harry kept a special shelf which was an altar of curry powders, poppadoms, chutneys and Bombay Duck. A recent 'line' at Sprogget & Sons, following upon the post-war craze for Chinese food, was tinned bamboo shoots, chop-suey and fried prawns. He even had the odd jar of caviar and if Harry had told me he kept his own sturgeon fisheries on the Volga, I shouldn't have disbelieved him.

Sprogget's was, in fact, the answer to Sylvia's fears about having to shop at a 'one-eyed village store'. There were many other shops in the village, but Sprogget's dabbled in most things and could be persuaded to try almost everything that modern canning and bottling had to offer. And as long as Sprogget, his son and daughters continue to function, there will be no need for any inhabitant of Codiham to travel up to London to stock up in exotic foodstuffs. Indeed, I would go further than this and assert that the Sproggets of this world have done more to civilize the countryside since the Second World War than any other visible factor.

But, I nearly forgot: it was Harry who set us[1] hot on the trail of Codiham's night life. When leaving an order one day – always with an eye to new business – Harry showed Sylvia a tin of frogs' legs: 'I must be the first man in Codiham to stock this,' he added proudly. 'Special order for the Halloween supper up at Miss Bronwen's.'

'Hallowe'en supper?' I echoed, always quick on the uptake when there was a hint of a party. 'What happens there?'

'Aaah,' drawled old Harry, winking. 'You know the saying, "us be proper wicked down at Codgem". There be rare goings on every Hallowe'en, but the party doesn't get started till after midnight. But I mustn't say more than that. Wouldn't be fair.'

I was determined to get to the bottom of these 'rare goings on' after midnight, so I straight away popped over to the Bearpits to seek out 'Sailor' Thompsett.

---

[1] My wife, who has corrected these proofs, asks me to substitute 'me' for us.

' "Sailor",' I asked. 'Who is Miss Bronwen?'

'Bronwen Pritchard, you mean. Oh, she's a "furriner". Leastways I suppose you might say that in another five years she'll be a real Codgemite. She's bin 'ere ten years now and if Codgem 'ad a Mayor and I was 'im, I'd give 'er the freedom of the place. A proper good, wicked 'un is Miss Bronwen.'

This sounded promising, for I knew that a 'proper good, wicked un' was high praise coming from 'Sailor'. And with a little eavesdropping here and a few discreet questions there I learned quite a lot about 'Miss Bronwen'. She was, it appeared, the fairy godmother of the artists of Codiham.

Ever since a confirmed alcoholic named Flinders had put up at the Merry Damsel for a night in 1919 and stayed on to turn a greenhouse into a studio there had been artists in the village. Flinders had been the most notorious as his greenhouse studio was in full view of any passers-by in Silk Lane and, though he sometimes painted, he was more often stretched out drunk on the floor, or cuddling the dairy-maid whom he occasionally 'borrowed' as a model. Before Flinders died of cirrhosis of the liver he had persuaded some of his fellow artists to join him in Codiham and from such raffish beginnings an artists' colony slowly sprang up.

Following the Flinders tradition, all Codiham artists adopted the Hole in the Wall as their recreational headquarters. When I arrived in Codiham there were ten of them all living within a stone's throw of one another on one side of the Green. None was famous, only three were professionals and they lived for the most part a frugal, if not an abstemious existence. Bronwen Pritchard was one of the exceptions. It was generally supposed that she had private means. At any rate she owned an expensive Queen Anne cottage on Cucking Green and had spent a good deal of her own money in converting a cowshed into a communal studio where, once a year, the Codiham Artists' Society presented an exhibition of their own work.

Prior to the acquisition of the cowshed the local artists had used their living-rooms, bedrooms, tool-sheds and even outhouses as galleries. They belonged to no 'school' of their own and insisted that their only connexion with one another was that they were one another's neighbours. But Bronwen changed this spirit of independence. As president of the Artist's Society she insisted that their future existence depended on their ability to live communally. Not, it might be added, that they carried this to the extent of having a communal kitchen, or of subsidizing each other. But they found that the studio provided an attractive setting for their wares and, during the summer months, brought them a few casual customers.

Bronwen herself was a natural publicist and she had managed to make the society known as far afield as Soho, Bloomsbury and Chelsea and even persuaded a Royal Academician to open one of their exhibitions. But even publicity can have its disadvantages; it brought in its wake second-hand dealers out for a 300 per cent quick profit and an invasion of London artists to compete for the three prizes which the society offered annually.

Bronwen Pritchard encouraged the ten local artists to turn their attention to something more than charcoal drawings, water-colours and oils. She started sculptoring and pottery classes and coaxed some of the village teenagers into making lino-cuts and designing wallpaper. She herself specialized in paintings of Romany life, in which she had made a special study. Some said she had been jilted by a Tzigane cabaret singer in Budapest before the war. Yet, ironically, Bronwen was best known locally for her home-brewed perry and cynics said that her perry was better than her painting.

This was all very illuminating, but the question remained how to be invited to her Hallowe'en party. 'Sailor' Brown assured me that if Bronwen was giving a party, there would be plenty to drink – 'enough perry to sink a battleship'. But somehow I thought that 'Sailor' was being a little too reticent on the subject of the party. And 'Sailor' was never reticent without a purpose.

'The purpose' was revealed when he asked me to join him over at the Damsel for a 'quiet one'. Once inside the 'snug', looking craftier than usual and having bought me a pint of October Ale, he asked just a little too casually whether I was 'doing anything on Saturday'.

'Well,' I added cautiously. 'I was thinking of watching football.'

'Would it matter much where you watched it?'

'Why?'

'Oh, nothing. I just thought you might like a change. Now a little run over to Tenterden ud do you good and there b'ain't such a bad football team there.'

'What the hell is all this leading to? Why should I go to Tenterden to watch football when I can perfectly well watch it in Codiham?'

'It's like this, sir. Sam Perkins and me thinks as 'ow it ud 'elp us no end if you was to do a bit o' spyin' for us at Tenterden. Next month we are due to play 'em and it ud be a great 'elp if somebody gave 'em the once over. Well, I was thinking – and Sam agrees – that if you, as a writing man, could pop over there and give us the low-down like, some sort of plan of tactics could be worked out to fair razzle 'em.'

'Who do you think I am? Matt Busby?'

'Well, you allus takes an intelligent interest in football and, wots more, you could put on paper all their weaknesses and strengths. You allus notices if the right-back is slow on the turn, or if he can be beaten on his left side more easily than his right. You usually manage to spot 'ow some of these new-style wingers lies well back and draws the full-backs out of position.'

'Hum! I suppose you want me to bring back a diagram of the pitch, to mark the spot X where it's usually so bogged down with mud that the ball sticks there and then to plot the one dry, grassy track on the wings so that Jim Bricknell will know where to boot his clearances.'

'That's just the idea, sir. And, if you can manage to do this, I think I can suitably reward you.'

'I can't go accepting bribes as a vice-president of Codiham United. But I can tell you what you might be able to do.'

'I've guessed that already. You want to go to Bronwen Pritchard's party, don't you?'

'And how do you know that?' I asked, with a pretence of not caring less.

'Ah, I know you're a proper lover of parties, sir. It's writ all over you.'

'Well, you'd better make it two invitations unless you want to break up the McCormick household.'

.   .   .   .   .

Sure enough when I got back home Bronwen Pritchard herself telephoned the invitations. We were advised to 'come in something informal and to bring an object which, when touched in the dark by a stranger, could pass for one of the unpleasanter parts of the anatomy'.

Sylvia had doubts. Not so much about what to wear as to the selection of an 'object'. The idea, as far as we could gather, was that at midnight the lights in the communal studio would be extinguished and Bronwen, dressed as a witch, went round with the objects on a tray. Each person, previously well fortified with perry, then had to guess what particular part of the anatomy he, or she, was supposed to be touching. On the telephone, with Bronwen breathlessly bubbling over with excitement, this game sounded both bizarre and obscure. Or, to use a more apt Sussex expression, chuckle-headed.

Hallowe'en had apparently at one time been a major festival in Codiham's life. But in Victorian days such goings-on were considered unseemly and the formal celebrations of the night on which witches and hobgoblins were supposed to come out and play gave place to more informal, but probably much less respectable frolics on Cucking Green. By custom the girls of the village dressed up as witches and collected for charity, which, I suspect, was a mere excuse for levity.

Sylvia rather pointedly rebuked me for interpreting Bronwen's phrase, 'the unpleasanter parts of the anatomy', as an excuse for rudery, adding that contact in the dark with any part of the anatomy unclothed could be unpleasant. On the basis of this reasoning we selected two grapes which, we hoped, might under cover of darkness pass as substitutes for the eyes of a human being.

With the two sticky grapes in an envelope marked 'Eyes', we set off to the Merry Damsel to stoke up our waning courage *en route*. Bronwen had indicated that no one should arrive before closing-time, as she felt sure that everybody would like to work up into a party mood first.

'This party,' Sylvia had said, 'sounds the nearest thing to an orgy since Nero fiddled while Rome burned.'

'That,' interrupted a voice from behind us, 'is a massive understatement. Nero never had Bronwen's perry.'

The voice was that of 'Doc' Gillebrand, our G.P. He was tall, young and sufficiently dashing and well-mannered in a bed-side sense to be the darling of Codiham's female population. 'Nothing whatever to do with being young, or dashing,' he used to tell me maliciously, 'but simply because I please the women by giving the men-folk hell.'

This was a most irritating habit of his. I never quite knew whether it was a leg-pull, or a homily. He, a bachelor, was always having the temerity to tell my wife that I ought to help with the washing-up. 'All men should be able to cook, sew, iron, wash up and clean the boiler. Treat the husbands rough and keep 'em tough, that's the right attitude.'

He was, however, a conscientious G.P. who, having worked in an industrial area where the National Health Service always functions more smoothly than in suburban and rural areas, made no attempt to distinguish between one class of patients and another. 'Doc' Gillebrand had a Freudian complex and insisted on psychiatric treatment for almost everything. Nor did he sign a piece of paper and pass his patients on to a consultant. As he neither played golf, nor had any hobbies, as far as one could tell, he was quite prepared to stay up half the night to listen to patients pouring out their phobias and anxiety-neuroses to him. He collected neuroses, complexes and case-histories of depressives, schizophrenics and straight-forward malingerers as another man would collect stamps.

'I suppose,' I said, possibly a little sarcastically, 'that you are going to Bronwen's to do a little psychiatric research.'

'Good heavens, yes! I learn more at her Hallowe'en parties in a night than I do as a G.P. in a year. Should be some excellent case-histories on show tonight, including your own.'

'My case-history, as you call it, will be securely padlocked tonight. I am coming strictly as an observer.'

'Pity. I had hoped you might let your hair down for once now that you are away from that typewriter. Can't think how your wife manages to keep sane listening to you banging away all day and night.'

'She types, too,' I added, defensively.

'Ah, I suspected as much. Always thought you were a slave-driver. Rigid type, that's you. A creator of manic-depressive conditions.'

But this badinage ceased when we arrived at the studio. Bronwen's art class had been responsible for the décor for the party, taking as their theme that 'blasted heath' of which Macbeth spoke. Fir trees in tubs were spaced around the room and the stuffed owls and buzzards in their branches provided a suitably eerie atmosphere in the dim light of green-shuttered lanterns. About a score of people were seated on the floor on cushions eating hot dogs around a witch's cauldron containing perry. I didn't see Harry Sprogget's frogs' legs either in the tin, or out of it. I assumed, correctly as it turned out, that they had been specially purchased to represent some obscure part of the anatomy. 'Sailor' Thompsett, looking like a character in Dylan Thomas's *Adventures in the Skin Trade*, was dangling a beer bottle on the end of one forefinger and singing a raucous ditty about 'The time I caught her bending in the cowshed'.

I had no time to take in anything else before Bronwen, wearing a witch's hat and a black dress that might have been a modish 'sack', or a shroud for all I knew, handed me a glass of perry. In the green light and the pea-soup fog of cigarette smoke her oval face, with no make-up and blobs of eye-shadow, made her look like Mata Hari masquerading as the Witch of Endor.

I make no apologies for digressing at this stage on the subject of perry and East Sussex drinks in general. It is a great mistake to think that Bordeaux and the Médoc are the greatest wine-producing districts in the world. East Sussex can beat them both in quantity and ingenuity, if not in quality. There is none of your nonsense about 'pressing' and 'racking'; the aim is to make sure that every cottage has a permanent stock of something that will cheer.

Codiham was a village of wine-makers. Sir Oswald Thyme produces a rather chalky wine from his own grapes which he delights in decanting for the purpose of pricking the pomposity of guests who claim they can tell a Clos de Vougeot 1921 blindfolded. In fact one of them mistook a Chateau Codiham 1949 for a Burgundy of 1909, though this was hardly a compliment as Mr. André Simon tells us that the Burgundies of that year, though pleasant when young, 'acquired a faint bitterness with age and a more objectionable rabbit hutch bouquet at a later stage.'

But most of the villagers, whether farm labourers' wives, retired fishermen, or serious-minded producers of home-made wine with an eye to making a few surreptitious shillings, relied not on the grape for the source of their vintages, but on pears, dandelion, elderberry, parsnips, cowslips, turnip, rhubarb, potatoes and strawberries. *Bouquet* was to them unimportant; the main object was to get the maximum alcholic content from the least expensive medium. They had their 'vintage years' of which they could sometimes be persuaded to talk. A 'Codgem Dandelion 1947' was rated a first-class drink, but the best perry (other than that which Bronwen made from her own recipe) was pre-war. And I am told that in two years' time a 'Codgem Strawberry 1959' will hold its own with any of them.

Bronwen's perry certainly followed the maxim of concentrated alcoholic content. You didn't say 'it's smooth, but it will never be a *great* wine,' nor did you suggest that it had 'body'. A connoisseur, holding it up to the light, would have condemned it for a certain muddiness. But there was no mistaking its potency. As 'Sailor' Thompsett, who was wisely sticking to beer, with a pint tankard in one hand and the bottle still balanced on the forefinger of the other, remarked: 'Perry fair makes you curious.'[1]

I do assure you it is much more fun to make perry, or parsnip wine than to lay in a cellar of French vintages the bill for which always seems to arrive at the same time as the rate-demand, the electricity account and notices for the renewals of various insurance policies. One of the attractions of living in the country is to be able to impress your friends with the superiority of country living. And I find that as a general rule, reprehensible as it may be, they are much more impressed by the quantity in, than

---

[1] That degree of intoxication which can most charitably be described as unsteady.

the quality of, your cellar. To be able to offer several *apéritif* perries before a meal, two bottles of vintage cider with it and a loganberry liqueur afterwards is very much better for one's pocket and for one's guests' unfathomable capacity for drink than to slip out of the room and squeeze a few thimblefuls of expensive gin from the last half-bottle and hope that the one bottle you have of Chateau Canon La Gaffelière 1934 will run to a glass and a half each.

It is also a good rule to stick to the 'wine of the country' when drinking, whether that means sherry in Spain, Irish whisky or Guinness in Dublin, or ale, beer and home-made wines in Sussex. Perry, I must confess, I have not yet been able to produce to my entire satisfaction. My own belief is that one needs an old-fashioned 'copper' in which to brew it and a careful hand with the yeast. Bronwen won't divulge her own recipe.

But I can speak with some authority on other local wines. The first essential is to make up your mind to produce the stuff. Providing you have the requisite thirst and taste for it, this may sound easy enough. The truth is, however, that as you have to wait a very long time before you can safely drink the wine, one is apt to postpone the operation and to go out to the 'local' and buy something instead.

On the other hand it is equally a mistake to let the liquid, once made, stand for two months before bottling. Some people do this under the impression that it will increase the alcoholic strength of the wine. In fact, it makes little difference in this respect. All that happens is that, if the wine is left to ferment in an unstrained state, too much air will get to the wine, adding all kinds of undesirable bacteria.

Having four elder trees in our garden, we personally favour a wine made from this source. There are several methods of brewing elderberry wine, but I would advise anyone to eschew the more popular recipes as, more often than not, they turn out to be cough-mixtures and throat-gargles rather than an honest tipple. Some elderberry wines are undoubtedly efficacious as a remedy for coughs and sore throats, but I am prescribing for the wine cellar, not the medicine-cabinet.

The Oast House, Mark III, Elderberry Wine, variously christened by our franker friends as *Lacrimae McCormicki*, Graymalkin's Posset and Elderado, is made each year with ritualistic fervour and much argument as to whether it is time to experiment with a Mark IV. You first of all boil a gallon of water and three and a half pounds of sugar until the water is perfectly clear. Then, taking about three pounds of elder blossoms, and making sure there is no green, you pop them into a bowl, pour in the boiling water and add sliced lemons and just under an ounce of hops. This concoction is left until it is lukewarm, when you sprinkle lightly with yeast.

The bowl is now put away in a dark corner for six days, after which you strain it, throw away what can only be described as the debris and add half a pound of barley. Don't think your task is now done. The bowl must be well covered and again put away in the aforementioned dark corner for another eighteen days. It is advisable to ring the kitchen calendar on the date on which this 'laying down' is done and to make a further mark to remind you when to recommence operations. Otherwise you may find yourselves producing not the Mark III, but the Mark I Elderberry Wine. On our first attempt we completely forgot about the bowl until five weeks afterwards when, fetching wood-logs from the cellar, I stumbled over it. What was left of the Mark I was drinkable, but not palatable.

However, assuming you have taken precautions that you won't forget, after eighteen days one strains the mixture once more and then bottles it. Be sure to cork your bottles lightly for the first month, otherwise you may be roused in the night by the sounds of several loud explosions. We lost most of our Mark II this way, not to mention several hours' sleep. When the month is up you just tighten the corks and then sit back and stiffen your resolution not to drink any of the stuff for at least another two months.

But, of course, you must have the patience of a bird-watcher, the placid temperament of an Eskimo and the strength of mind of a reformed alcoholic to achieve the right results.

This takes one a very long way from Bronwen's party, but I hope in the process I have shown that, if you prefer cheap liquor to being a wine snob, there are some useful tips to be picked up in Codiham.

If this party had been in Chelsea, it could easily have developed into a clinically sophisticated charade of Hallowe'en. But the décor did not oppress one; there was no attempt to be clever, no hint of the artists patronizing the plebs; the potted fir trees with their stuffed owls and buzzards were at least symbols one could grasp. Bronwen's genius as a party-giver was that she knew how to be jolly without being hearty, how to blend the bibulous with the artistic, the drinkers who sing at the slightest provocation with those who prefer to go into a corner and natter, the dancers and the practical jokers, the natural revellers from the Hole in the Wall with the few who might be tempted to indulge in Beatnik exhibitionism.

H

It was a remarkable cross-section of local society. 'Sailor' Thompsett, with his sea shanties and some lurid, old-time Sussex Hallowe'en ditties, contributed to the gaiety of the evening without monopolizing it. He was devoted to Bronwen, whom he had described to me as 'a reg'lar brencheese[1] friend, she is not like a good many, after what they can get.' Bronwen, too, had a high opinion of 'Sailor', and he was a natural guest at the party not only because of his close association with the artists at the Hole in the Wall, but on account of his working as an occasional model for them at half-a-crown an hour. There is no doubt that 'Sailor' is a man of many parts and I should not be in the least surprised if I learned he worked for M.I.5, the N.I.D. and the F.B.I., nor that he was a missionary of the Mormon Church.

The anatomical game, though it threatened to become out of hand when 'Ginger' Pearson produced a coco de mer from the Seychelles, spared everyone's blushes owing to the rigid black-out enforced by Bronwen while it was being played. General Gordon was firmly convinced that the Seychelles were the site of the Garden of Eden and named the coco de mer 'forbidden fruit'. Whether he saw what 'Ginger' Pearson saw, I cannot say, but in size, shape and appearance down to its tufts of fibre-like pubic hairs it looks exactly like a naked female pelvis.

'Ginger' Pearson was generally regarded as the genius of Codiham's artistic colony. He disdained water-colours and formal oil paintings, demanding nothing less than a whole wall for his masterpieces. In this respect he was one up on Eva, for he had painted what was supposed to depict 'an allegory of Man's Subconscious Mind' on the four walls of the Hole in the Wall 'loo'. It more nearly represented the interior of a fifth-rate Algerian brothel. 'Ginger' whispered to me that I must come to one of his 'monthly orgies' sometime. I have since heard that he was an acquaintance of Aleister Crowley and that he once conducted black magic ceremonies at Westhurst Abbey, following a boozy Midsummer's Eve party in Ghost Wood. This is another aspect of Codiham night life which I have yet to investigate.

'Bifty' Etheridge was an ex-R.N.V.R. officer who sported an enormous black beard and described himself as 'a cartoonist in search of a job'. By which he meant that he had been rebuffed by Fleet Street and managed to exist somewhat precariously by doing cartoons at ten bob a nob at various public dinners. He walked for miles across the Weald, sketching as he went, but few people seemed to buy his work. Marigold Strawson was rather a sweet, unaffected girl, who shared a cottage with a

[1] A true friend.

fiercely possessive female who smoked cigars and designed posters for the less inhibited seaside resorts. She also made pottery and acted as communal model for her fellow artists.

Such 'nights out' as Bronwen's party didn't occur every week, or even every month in Codiham. But there were enough of such occasions to satisfy one's normal urge for parties without the risk of being committed to a surfeit of 'dates' in one's diary. There was the Hopper's Ball on Cucking Green in mid-September, Flossie Whitcombe's Venetian Carnival on the Dentical, the Morris Dancers' annual visit to the Bearpits when a licence extension was always granted and, at Christmas time, a round of punch parties after church on Sundays at various farms and private houses. There is also a good deal of 'night life' which, to one who is still a 'furriner', is as yet taboo. One hears a whisper here, a veiled hint there, but, on making inquiries, everyone rapidly changes the subject. Such 'goings on' are invariably referred to as a 'cab', which in Sussex dialect may be roughly defined as a small number of persons secretly united in the performance of some nocturnal undertaking. The phrase is probably a corruption of the French *cabaler* and may have been introduced by the Huguenots, though one hardly associates them with such proceedings.

There is always a suggestion of brimstone and necromancy about these 'cabs', whether they are mentioned in connexion with 'Ginger' Pearson's orgies, in the Singing Cricket tea-rooms, where the youth of the village gather, or among the inhabitants of the remoter cottages. This may be merely a curious manifestation of Codiham's delight in advertising and romanticizing its 'wickedness'; it is always difficult to separate bar-room chatter from legend, but there is abundant evidence that black magic was practised in the neighbourhood a hundred years ago and some very strange parties are still supposed to take place on Midsummer's Eve.

'It were long ago it all started,' says Young George, 'when there bain't be so many lasses in the village. My grandpa did say as 'ow there was never enough lasses to go round, not even at the bough houses. And it were then that the men, so starved of 'oomen, did take themselves off to Ghost's Wood in quest of a randy night. 'Tis terrible to say so today, though the papers they do tell many terrible things still, but if they couldn't find 'oomen, they tuk a ship[1], or even a swan from the Pond. It were the bumboo juice wot did it and the end were nearly allus Lewes Assizes.'

There is nothing worse than that *coitus interruptus* of drinking when

[1] Sheep.

in London, one goes into a bar, has a few drinks and comes out without having spoken to a soul, the atmosphere so redolent of depression that you could almost feel it flapping round you like a thick, black curtain. This couldn't happen in Codiham. To enter the Merry Damsel is always an adventure, with the prospect of being asked to 'drop in and have a nightcap' by some friendly couple. If the Bearpits is much more down to earth, more a place for serious farming business, or the even more serious affair of marbles, one could never fail to find mischief, if in quest of it, at the Hole in the Wall. Once accepted as one of the Hole's regulars, one has the choice after closing time of tackling some of 'Ginger' Pearson's parsnip wine, having perry and biscuits at Bronwen's, or being lured over to the *Dainty Doris*, high and dry on the outgoing Dentical, for a 'drop of wallop' with 'Sailor'.

9. *Fun among the fairy-sparks*

Do not think that we spent the first winter in the Oast House by indulging in a continual round of Codiham's night life, or that, as the previous chapter may have suggested, we were always to be found in either the Merry Damsel, the Bearpits or the Hole in the Wall.

Nor should you imagine that the chapter-heading which I have just written is meant to convey that we abandoned all decency and embarked on some orgiastic dream fantasy in the world of bumboo and perry.

I will explain the meaning of my chapter-title in due course. For the moment, irritating though it may be to postpone my explanation, I must somewhat prosaically report that during the winter there was a very great deal to be done in the Oast House itself and much planning for the transformation of the tamed jungle in the spring. We had been in our new home long enough to realize a few of the Awful Mistakes which one inevitably makes when attempting any unusual conversion for the first time, either with, or without, the assistance of those mandarin-like spivs who call themselves architects.

One such Awful Mistake was the failure to provide the house with enough cupboards and built-in wardrobes and another was that we so completely miscalculated the number of books we possessed that they not only spilt over into the loft, but actually invaded both 'loos' and the kitchen. Which, as I pointed out to Sylvia, was not a bad thing, for it is much better to have the works of Mrs. Beaton and *Tante Marie* alongside the cooker (as a gentle but firm reminder of what can be achieved) than to have them mouldering forgotten in a box-room. As to turning the 'loos' into libraries, this is a subject on which I hold strong views. I am of the opinion, especially when some crashing bore has wormed his (or her) way into the house, that it is as well to have an escape-hole. And what better than a lavatory with a secure lock, a pleasant view and a book-shelf within easy reach? This to my mind is one simple means of doubling the standard of living without working any harder.

Unlike Eva I am unable to write in a lavatory, but I insist it should be furnished with some worth-while pictures, even if only prints from *La Vie Parisienne*, or pages from *Men Only*, a row of at least a dozen books, a box of cigarettes and the few odd cigars one is able to salve after Christmas and – this is most important – a heater.

Fortunately there were all manner of nooks, crannies, recesses and ugly corners which could easily be converted into cupboards. Unfortunately the Oast House attracted moths as prolifically as the proverbial candle and we had to spend a fortune investing in all manner of sprayers, anti-moth pumps and cardboard devices which you tie up and hope for the best. But even such a formidable armament as this failed to defeat the moths. The cardboard devices worked only for about two weeks and the instructions for the use of the various sprays were so full of don'ts that one felt it was safer not to use them at all. Either you risk starting a fire if you spray near a light, or you ruin your wife's one and only fur coat, or the stuff kills the cat and poisons anyone who goes near it afterwards. Always excepting the wretched moths. It took us two years to realize that the best answer is still the old-fashioned moth-ball. No shop-keeper will tell you this; he will probably pretend they aren't made any more. Don't believe him. If you live in the country, moth-balls are essential unless you are prepared to buy a complete new wardrobe every year. I speak from bitter experience. And don't try to tell me that several moth-proof bags, or camphor-wood boxes are the answer. Not only is this method as costly as it is to furnish a single room, but it's the devil of a job opening up all that lot every time you want a new shirt.

Dick Pride is all very well in his way, but when it comes to putting right Awful Mistakes, the best and cheapest plan is to find a Master Dobbs.[1] Our discovery in this line was Jim Bricknell, who, apart from being a competent grave-digger and a lusty full-back, can destroy wasps' nests, kill rats, make cupboards, procure perry at a reasonable price and, when

[1] A Sussex expression for a 'house-fairy', or Jack-of-all-trades.

in the mood, have quite astonishing brainwaves. He is a man who really ought to be landed on a desert island and left there for six months. Not as a punishment, but as an experiment in testing human ingenuity.

'If you lives in the country,' he says, 'it's chuckle-headed to throw anything away. There's not a thing as ull not come in useful.'

I must say he found plenty to prove his point. From the hollow at the end of the garden he retrieved an old oilskin and some boots which he said 'ud do fine for me grave-digging,' an ancient lavatory seat which he asked if he could have to 'do up my lavender' and a collection of junk which he offered to me with the air of one distributing largesse.

If it wasn't largesse, at least it turned out to be extremely useful, which just shows what a Town Clot I am and how deeply cunning and intelligent is the country mind. Out of the junk came forth enough timber and slates to repair the derelict horse-box in the grounds and convert it into a combined store-house and potting-shed, not to mention various hooks, rusty hinges, sticks, biscuit tins, jam jars and pot-hangers, all of which Jim put to good use. I do believe he pretty well furnished the store-house out of this junk and he even made toy men-o'-war out of wood chippings, thus tremendously impressing Anthony by his versatility. But his best finds were a beer barrel, which he painted, polished and eventually turned into a handsome garden-table and the cast-off cowl of some other oast which had been tossed away under the fir trees. I was all for chopping it up for firewood, though we already had enough of that from what Eva had retrieved to last us a year. But not Jim. He worked away on that battered cowl for weeks in between his grave-digging and playing football and the outcome was a perfectly good summerhouse.

By late February I was beginning to feel the urge to escape from the pressing problems of developing and expanding a home. I had an ultra-mundane, spring-is-round-the-corner *frisson*, a restless desire to go out and explore, to extend my horizons. It is all very well living in the country, but darned stupid if you don't take a look at it. Up in that ivory tower of a study I had for some months been content to gaze in bovine fashion across the Green, to watch the skaters on the frozen pond. Now I raised my sights and wistfully contemplated the merging of the meadows beyond Codiham with the vast, grey-green sweep of Romney Marsh, fading into the swirling, dancing mists of late February.

The Reverend Richard Barham, author of *Ingoldsby Legends*, said that the world consisted of 'Europe, Asia, Africa, America and Romney Marsh.' And, indeed, the Marsh at first glimpse, from almost any angle, has the immensity of a whole continent. Also, having had a whole winter in which to read about the Marsh, I had begun to feel it really was invested with some kind of supernatural aura. The fact that Lambarde, writing in 1570, had said it was 'evil in winter, grievous in summer, but never good' only whetted my appetite further.

'Bifty' Etheridge introduced me to the Marsh and, unwittingly, provided the title of this chapter. Having chatted rather desultorily one night over a beer, 'Bifty' suddenly suggested: 'What about you and I fornicating among the fairy-sparks tomorrow night?'

I knew that 'Bifty' had a one-track mind on the subject of carnal adventure, but until now he had not included me in his more lecherous escapades. 'And what are fairy-sparks?' I asked suspiciously.

'Ah! I thought that would fox you. Don't be alarmed: I'm not suggesting we should go out importuning, or anything like that, if that's what you're thinking. I'm thoroughly heterosexual in my tastes. No, old boy, to "fornicate" has a distinct meaning of its own in Sussex. Really, the natives have a perfectly delightful way with the English language. "To fornicate" means to explore, to dawdle, to waste time pleasantly. And "fairy-sparks" is not a name for a new type of queer, but merely what the locals call the will-o'-the-wisps, those blue, flickering phosphorescent lights that appear over the Marsh.'

Now 'Bifty' is an inveterate leg-puller and I wasn't going to take this information on his word alone. In case you, too, find it hard to believe there is a pleasanter and more charitable interpretation of 'fornication' than that usually provided by vengeance-invoking divines, I must refer you to a more enlightened clergyman. The Reverend W. D. Parish, a former vicar of Selmeston, compiled in 1875 a *Dictionary of the Sussex Dialect*, an admirable handbook for anyone going to live in the remoter parts of the county. In this book, with admirable disregard for the Victorian reticence of his day, he unashamedly defines the verb 'to fornicate' as 'to dawdle, or waste time.'

In Parish's day there were three distinct Sussex dialects – East Sussex, Mid-Sussex and West Sussex. Little remains of the purely Mid-Sussex dialect; the coming of the main line to the coast towns and building development at Crawley and Haywards Heath have killed it off. But in the more inaccessible villages of East and West Sussex the robust, imaginative English of an earlier day still thrives. Romney Marsh, as one would expect, has retained its individuality in this respect and you can still hear the true dialect in Codiham and other villages away from the main roads. The native cussedness and obstinacy of Sussex reveals itself unexpectedly in both dialect and pronunciation. The former is typified by a refusal to use any long-winded, or fancifully pretentious name and deliberately to debunk such rodomontade talk by a form of jocular verisimilitude. Thus your average Sussex gardener of the old school will not speak of chrysanthemums, but of 'Christy anthems'. As to pronunciation, this is most easily distinguished by the long a's as in 'larmentable' and the transposition of vowels. You don't boil an egg in Codiham, you 'biol' it; you talk of a 'voilent' not a violent man. Double e is pronounced as i and i becomes double e – e.g. sheep are 'ship' and mice are 'meece'.

But the real joy of this part of the country lies not in any juggling with vowels or grammar (though heaven knows they do plenty of that), but in the unexpected and spontaneous use of words in an unusual context. Sometimes this can give one a sudden jolt, as for instance when Eva related how she 'fornicated across Cucking Green last night', or when Jim Bricknell initimated that he was 'properly flogged' when he arrived home. But it was not Jim's Belinda who had suddenly developed a passion for flagellation; all he meant to convey was that he was tired out.

But, back to 'Bifty' Etheridge. It was 'Bifty's' suggestion that I should accompany him on a pub crawl across the continent – the fifth continent of Romney Marsh, that is. 'Bifty', as I have indicated, was a great walker, but even he jibbed at the idea of doing the Marsh entirely on foot. So, embarking in his ancient Ford early one morning, we set off loaded with sandwiches, a flask of perry and all the paraphernalia of his profession. 'Must take some perry to put us in the right mood for seeing blue lights tonight,' he commented.

The title 'Marsh' is really a misnomer. It has been so well drained by deep dykes that to all intents and purposes it is firm land. At one time it was a breeding ground for mosquitoes and as late as the end of the eighteenth century was so ravaged by malaria and ague that even the men who farmed there lived up-country if they could. Absentee landlord-ism was the rule rather than the exception. Those who had to dwell in such unsalubrious terrain couldn't even find a doctor on the Marsh; their imaginative, if amateurish cure for the ague was to put a live spider, wrapped up in a gingerbread nut, in their tea.

I doubt whether anywhere else in Britain you will find so many sheep as on Romney Marsh. One hears a great deal about the decline of sheep-farming in this country, but the Marsh would gladden the heart of the most enthusiastic devotee of mutton. Sheep still depend on the shepherd and the dog and broad acres of grassy upland, and the former, as depicted

in the old-time cartoon, complete with crook, has long since given way
to a casual (in more senses than one) farm labourer who thinks it is all
rather a bore and much more profitable to be filling in his football
coupons than keeping an eye on sheep. But the Marsh has in some way
survived as a pasturage despite the decline in sheep-farming, despite the
fact that, far from being upland, much of it is below sea-level. Codiham
Church tower and steeple and many of the other exquisite perpendicular
'woollen churches' of Kent and East Sussex owe their existence to
Romney Marsh sheep.

Estimates vary, but I should say there must be anything upwards of
160,000 sheep in this area. A mahogany-skinned, wrinkled old 'looker' –
as the Marshmen call their shepherds – told 'Bifty' and I in a pub at
Brookland that 'it were Noah who made Marsh ship famous. 'ee brought
'is Ark up past Rye and 'ee tuk one look at our ship and said "I'll 'ave
two of un aboard the Ark as if the likes of they can scrape a living 'ere,
they'll do purty well anywhere".'

However, we didn't make the trip across the Marsh just to gaze at
sheep and I am not going to say that Marsh mutton is the best in the
world. It tends to be rather coarse, though in summer it is certainly one
of the primest of meats and, as these are salt marshes, it can be cooked
and served as *mouton de pré-salé* without fear of indignant contradictions
from your friends.

We entered the Marsh by crossing the stone bridge over the Dentical
at Henty, the hamlet which adjoins Codiham, and then headed for Stone-
cum-Ebony. It is all a matter of opinion and temperament as to which is
the best way to approach the fifth continent. Much depends upon the time
of year and your mood. In November, on a really misty night, and if you
are in an adventurous vein, you might do worse than take the road from
Tenterden through Smallhythe, fill a flask with rum and your mind with
thoughts of Dr. Syn. Eerily, in the dancing mist, the road winds slowly
downhill, the countryside becoming bleaker as the Marsh draws nearer.
Down on the Marsh the mist takes on a diaphanous, opalescent quality
which causes it to play spookish tricks.

But only if you are sufficiently enterprising to leave the roads and strike
out boldly across the footpaths, will you find the Marsh's real treasures,
most of which, thank God, are securely hidden from the motorist. We
came back via Tenterden and found the night alive with 'fairy-sparks' and
the kaleidoscopic effects of mist and marsh gases. The mist will change
from an almost fluorescent pink in late afternoon to purple and sometimes
green at dusk and the gases create an illusion of bluish will-o'-the-wisps

hovering at reed height like so many miniature flying saucers from outer space.

Should you enter the Marsh from the opposite direction, via Lydd, you will see its wildest and least inhabited tract, unhappily the one area of the fifth continent threatened by politicians who talk glibly about doubling the standard of living in twenty-five years by sprinkling the countryside with nuclear reactors. Happily, Romney Marsh is vast enough to be able to absorb such monstrosities without being seriously affected, but no one can say with any degree of certainty what the effects will be on the agricultural way of life and one of the finest bird sanctuaries in Britain.

Romney Marsh must be a bird-watcher's idea of heaven. Apart from water-fowl, to whom it is an absolute paradise, you will find grey herons, poised silently for a kill, the bullying starlings pecking parasites from the sheep, an occasional swan gliding forlornly but majestically along the Military Canal which Pitt created; moorhens, shelducks in the snuggest creeks, magpies, herring gulls, and – in summer – larks and wagtails trilling and warbling in a feast of song. Rooks, crows and jackdaws hunt on the Marsh in day-time, returning to their homes in the elms at night. The fifth continent is really one all-embracing aviary. Here the lovely little goldfinch, so often heard but so rarely seen, vies with the greenfinch and the bluetit for charm and grace; the black tern can be discerned mating and, if you are very, very fortunate, the black redstart.

As a family we didn't formally take up bird-watching. It just happened. I had always rather scornfully regarded bird-watching as a form of psychiatric treatment for tired field-marshals who had filled their systems with bile and their memoirs with vitriol. But then I am apt to make wild generalizations of this sort. I soon learned that birds can be good company, sometimes uproariously so. Our kitchen window overlooks an open space of grass, backed with a variety of trees. Thus, when washing up, one can combine a dull chore with an absorbing hobby whatever the time of year. All you need to do to become a bird-watcher at the Oast House is to tear up all leaflets advertising washing-up machines and to keep alongside you at the kitchen sink one of those excellent books such as *The Observer's Book of Birds*, and, if you can afford it, binoculars. If you don't buy the washing-up machine, you *can* afford the binoculars. Then you bait the grass with substantial pieces of bread (preferably slightly moistened if the bread is hard) and, to encourage the blue tits, hang a piece of fat bacon on one of the trees. The washing-up may take a little longer, but one's education is considerably improved. A bird-bath will be a useful addition and I suggest that a concrete one is made as most of the bird-baths sold in the shops crack at the first frost, this being a prime aim of manufacturers in maintaining profits and avoiding the necessity for price reduction.

I would further suggest all beginner bird-watchers (I use this word in a strictly amateur sense) should write to a most enterprising and erudite salesman named Mr. Eric Wood, of Ombersley, Droitwich, Worcestershire. He will send you screeds of typed information with full details of the type of gadgets (all of which he can supply) that will make this bird game a festival of fun. These gadgets include, bird-tables, nesting compartments, tit and robin boxes, food arks, seed hoppers and nut-feeders.

Mr. Wood has coined a phrase for all this activity – birdmanship. He points out that, with the exception of wood pigeons, British birds actually help anyone who raises crops, providing he feeds and looks after them throughout the hard winter. Many birds like nuts, stale cake, fish-heads or meaty bones; insect-eaters should be given fat, or live foods, and apples and oranges are popular with them. Blackbirds and thrushes like ground oats made into a stiff paste with milk and water, soaked currants and lots of drinking water. Wrens are very partial to ants' eggs. Many of the wilder and more unusual birds can be enticed to one's garden by planting for them. A handful of sunflower seeds will attract attention when fully grown. One of the best bird trees is the mulberry, which is easily grown and has a long season.

My son kept a careful diary of birds observed. At first it consisted mostly of noting the ubiquitous sparrow, the nervous thrush, the hectoring, get-to-hell-out-of-it starling, the amazingly tame, orange-breasted robin and our favourite, the eager, fragile blue tit. Being earnest devotees of Lost Causes and dead agin' the government of starlings, we spent and wasted much time putting down the dishes and dashing out to chase away these bullies every time they chivvied a thrush out of a bird-bath so that they could preen themselves in dictatorial solitude.

But, as the months passed, the diary occasionally had more exciting notes. Early in March a wheatear arrived, presumably from across the Channel via the Marsh, hopping swiftly along the ground in a manner which has earned it the nickname of 'clod-hopper', easily recognized by the white patch at the base of its tail.

Then, during a belated spell of snow in March, came a challenging David to put the bullying Goliaths of the starling Gestapo to rout. A patch of snow had been swept to make access to the bread and bacon rind easier. On to this patch flew a tiny, obviously very young pied-wagtail. He gave no quarter to anyone, sparrows, chaffinches, robins or the few starlings that happened to be around. Clearly, he regarded the patch as his own preserve, and nobody else was allowed to do more than sneak an occasional scrap far distant from himself.

We began to look upon these birds as our own pets and it is a fact that, if you are in the country, you can acquire a variety of pets without giving yourself a great deal of work. The robin, perhaps, can most easily be coaxed into actually feeding from your hand and making a permanent home near by, but, apart from birds, there are many other unusual characters which can be induced to join the family. One such – and we have had him a long time now – is the hedgehog, unattractive perhaps when rolled up in a prickly ball, but with a most appealing, wistful look when you manage to get a close-up of his sharp, intelligent face.

A hedghog can be a boon for anyone owning a garden and should always be encouraged, as any gardener worth his pay will tell you. A hedgehog will destroy all manner of insect pests; it has a voracious appetite for its size and will devour worms and snails and even snakes. In this way it will amply repay you for adopting it, which is more than you can say for most pets which become pampered appendages.

The hedgehog has one fault – a penchant for lumbering over flower-beds and crushing them with his weight. The first indication we had of his presence was when, on consecutive mornings, we found our milk bottles totally empty, lying flat on the step outside the back-door, the metal-foil caps neatly punctured.

Deciding that a thief of some description was around, but unable to understand how he stole the milk without breaking the bottles, we put half a bottle of milk out one night as a bait. Then, taking it in turns, we watched for the culprit. Eventually Mr. Hedgehog arrived and, under our very noses, proceeded to edge the bottle from the upright position into one which left it lying across his body. After that it was quite easy for him to break the cap and suck out the precious liquid.

We couldn't afford to go on keeping so milk-happy a creature on such generous rations, so we instructed the milkman to put his wares inside the door of the kitchen porch and not outside. All the same we have continued to put a saucer of milk out each night and our friend is now quite unafraid of us.

But I think Anthony's diary tells the story of our tame hedgehog far more effectively than I can. Here are some of his notes, which, on the strict understanding that I pay him a percentage of royalties, he is prepared to let me crib:

'Mr. Hedgehog kills adder in the hollow. Adder bit first, but Mr. Hedgehog not worried. He bit adder across back, then ate him up, starting with the tail and working towards the head.'

[Author's note: the hedgehog would seem to be innoculated by nature against all snake bites.]

'Scooped up Mr. Hedgehog in a basket, carried him upstairs and tipped him out on the top stair. He rolled himself into a ball and then tumbled downstairs. Mr. Hedgehog seemed to enjoy this, for he climbed upstairs on his own and rolled down again. Just for fun.'

Since reading this I have always kept a very close look-out when going up or down stairs.

. . . . .

When one is in Romney Marsh one is most forcibly struck by the evanescent quality of its atmosphere; one's mind drifts dreamily between past and future so that the subconscious mind rises to the surface like a cork and bobs about on the ocean of eternity. Thus, to write about the Marsh is rather like tackling a fourth dimensional exercise. Neither time, nor place is of any consequence and that is why this chapter flits from one month to another and casually 'fornicates' from Marsh to home, from home to Marsh.

'Bifty' and I explored a good deal of it together. Always there was the unexpected to confront one with an impish challenge. Not only the 'fairy-sparks' which we saw on the way home, but Brookland Church whose steeple, with Lewis Carroll perverseness, stands on the ground beside it, and whose font bears the signs of the Zodiac. Or the sudden appearance of a treble rainbow which gives the landscape a touch of Corot. On the eastern side, where the Marsh becomes a wilderness of pebble, plants spring up out of the stones. I do not know about any desert blossoming as the rose, but even in so inhospitable a region as Dungeness the thousands of acres of pebble are in June a mass of colour – purple pink thrift and golden stonecrop form a regal cloak. How so many flowers can flourish in a bed of stones often feet deep and never less than six inches is a perpetual mystery.

The Marsh is, of course, an acquired taste. It is not until one ventures across it on foot and alone that it reveals all its charms. Even then you either love it or hate it, but whatever your view, its fascination is undeniable. Sign-posts are unreliable; there are few enough of them, but for some extraordinary reason they rarely give accurate information. And, as though to suggest this is a conspiracy of silence, many of the real Marshmen are reluctant to tell you the way. If they can be persuaded to suggest a route, the odds are it will be the wrong one. That this is not merely the view of a Town Clot, or an author trying to find a mystery where none exists, I would refer you to G. M. Rainbird's *Inns of Kent*. Of the sign-posts on the Marsh he says:

'These are not deliberately false – sometimes they mention a distant village, forgetting the one nearest. . . Bonnington is marked on all the maps and one can find it without much trouble, but the *Royal Oak* is another of life's little mysteries. That the *Royal Oak* exists in fact would seem to be confirmed, in that sundry barrels of good ale are consigned to it weekly by the brewers at Hythe and, in return, cash and cheques in payment thereof are received from time to time. Moreover, the writer was twice within a short distance carefully and precisely directed to this very inn, by people who looked as if they should know. He is by no means unobservant and, he thinks, has moderate intelligence, yet twice did he find himself in the next parish without seeing the trace of an inn.'

Perhaps in Romney Marsh we have the nucleus of a powerful anarchical underground which in the years ahead can be built up into the spearhead of a national movement to sabotage the Americanization of Britain, a trend to which all political parties consciously or unconsciously lend support. I do not make this comment in a Chestertonian or Bellocian frame of mind, for no one in his right senses would want to put the clock back as they did. But the Marshman, and I have noticed the same urge among many Codgemites, wants to keep his individuality. He doesn't want to go back to the Middle Ages, or to stay genuine progress but he detests unthinking invasions whether of an alien way of life, or, by the opening up of new arterial roads to make Britain a land fit only for road-hogs to live in. You can be within a mile of Codiham and ask a Codgemite the way to the village. 'Happen you want to go to Hastings?' he will reply.

'I said Co-di-ham,' the irritated motorist will repeat.

'Oh, ah think you want the main road. Better turn back and take the first on the left. There bain't no good way to Codgem.'

·   ·   ·   ·   ·

'Wee Walter', the tiny octogenarian marbles champion of the Bearpits, used to make a hobby of annoying motorists in this fashion. 'Wee Walter' would sit on the wooden bench at Four-wents and wait for some motorist to pull up and ask him which of the four roads to take. Four-wents was about a mile outside Codiham and many an exasperated traveller must have been misdirected by Walter's feigned stupidity.

'Why should I let un come and spoil our village with their stinking, dratted motor cars?' he asked me. 'If they be so chuckle-headed as not to know 'ow it's Codgem, not Co-di-ham, well, dang 'em, I says. Drat their noisy motor cars.'

A great character is 'Wee Walter'. Though raddled with rheumatism, almost crippled with arthritis, despite threats of 'giving up marbles next winter', he stays on as the most colourful member of the Codiham Bearbaiters' team.

Marbles still flourishes in the Sussex countryside as may be witnessed by the ferocious titles of some of the teams: the Codiham Bearbaiters, the Telcon Terribles, the Tinsley Green Tigers, the Copthorne Spitfires and Johnson Jets. There is even a British Marbles Board of Control, which has no constitution and no rules, but is extremely vocal when anyone suggests that women, too, can play marbles, as Lady Docker discovered when she asked for some tips in preparation for her appearance as a marbles player on a television programme.

''Oomen play marbles?' said 'Wee Walter' scornfully. 'Why they'd never learn the game in a hundred years. Why, I can split a pint pot with a flick of a marble. Wot 'ooman can do that?'

Codiham may not have taken part in the annual marbles champion-ship of England, held at the Greyhound Inn, Tinsley Green, in Sussex each Eastertide, but that, 'Wee Walter' will tell you is merely because 'we ain't spoilin' our holiday by prancing over to Tinsley Green and we doesn't 'old with all this publicity.

'Anyhow, we reckons as 'ow we 'ave the best marbles bed in the world and we're quite happy to stay at the Bearpits and leave the blobtitting[1] to the Copthorne Spitfires and the Arundel Mullets.'

Indeed, the Codiham Bearbaiters will ignore the evidence provided by the annual marbles championship at Tinsley Green and assure you seriously that 'none of they champions ud give us a bannicking[2] at the Bearpits.' And until and unless England's reigning champions accept this challenge, Codiham Bearbaiters will remain unconvinced.

[1] Tale-telling and boasting.
[2] Beating.

In my early visits to the Bearpits I was puzzled by the strange and bloodthirsty language used by the marbles players. I couldn't make out whether this was a den of thieves and thugs, or a hide-out for modern smugglers. There were whispers of 'tolleys' hidden in secret places at the inn and chatter about 'killers, slashers and terrors'.

'What are these tolleys you talk of?' I asked Walter one day.

'Tolleys?' he chuckled. 'Why tolleys is marbles.'

'Well, why do you hide them away?'

'Well, as you ought to know by now, "us be proper wicked down at Codgem", and tolleys ain't safe left lyin' around. Last time we played Henty Artfuls, one of they Artfuls stole a thousand tolleys from "Killer" Grist's box and more'n five-hundred from "Slasher" Butterwick. So since then we've hidden away most of our tolleys in the secret cupboards under the stairs of the Bearpits.'

April is the month when the marbles beds at the Bearpits see the most ferocious contests of the year. The Bearbaiters' chief opponents are the Henty Artfuls and the Marshmallows, a team of calloused, weather-beaten reprobates whose headquarters are said to be the Marsh Hare. But the Marsh Hare, like the Royal Oak at Bonnington, is difficult to find. I accept the existence of the Royal Oak, but I've never yet found the Marsh Hare.

The marbles beds at the Bearpits are sprinkled with sand and dampened to prevent the marbles rolling: 'it's as much of an art as preparing a wicket on Cucking Green,' said Walter. And doubtless done with far more nefarious intentions, I should imagine. For defeat is a word which the Bearbaiters will never allow in their vocabulary.

Each player has his own set of marbles; a tolley should not be more than half an inch in diameter. Forty-nine clay marbles are placed in the centre of the circular court for each team match, the odd number preventing a draw. The matches, according to Codiham rules, are played between two teams of six aside, each with his own tolley, or shooting marble, upon a ring six feet in diameter, known in Codiham as a 'bed'. Each player takes his turn to try to dislodge as many of the 'clays' as possible, without rolling his own tolley out of the ring. If he hits a 'clay' out and remains 'in', he may have another turn, and so make a run up to a theoretical maximum of twenty-five. If he is the first player for his side and achieves this distinction, then he will have won the game. If his tolley rolls out, he recovers it for his next turn. But if it fails either to knock another marble out, or to roll out itself, it must stay in the ring at the risk of being 'killed'.

I

The prize for the winners at the Bearpits during 'Marbles Week' is a hogshead of ale. There may be levity when the hogshead is actually won, but during the matches no one dares to make the mildest wisecrack. Each game is played out in the same sort of 'breathless hush' that characterized a certain Close. Beachcomber once referred to the sense of outrage engendered among the habituees at the Long Room at Lords when some cad struck a match on the pavilion railings. I sensed much the same reaction when I knocked my beer glass over during one of the marbles matches at the Bearpits. There was a prolonged silence; 'Slasher' Butterwick, who was just about to shoot his tolley, stayed his hand in mid-air and glowered at me. 'Wee Walter' looked so shocked that I might have been guilty of indecency; up shot his gnarled forefinger in a compelling gesture of reproof. Nor have I ever been allowed to forget my crime.

I believe that at Tinsley Green it is the custom to place the tolley to your nose before you shoot it. In Codiham each tolley is reverently kissed before a player shoots. I never could understand how 'Wee Walter' found a way to his mouth through the vast jungle of his beard. One moment the marble was visible in his hand, the next it had disappeared in the beard. There are several styles of tolley shooting. Some hold the hand about six inches above the ground; others let the hand touch the ground. 'Wee Walter' always squatted when shooting.

I feel sure this is a very inadequate description of marbles and experts will undoubtedly argue that the Codiham methods are not approved by the Marbles Control Board. There are all sorts of local variations of this game which was first introduced to Britain by the Romans. But to anybody thinking of taking up the game, I would urge a great deal of private practice before seeking to join a team like the Bearbaiters. If you have known what it is like to drop a dolly catch in the slips twice running, you will get some idea of the searing, silent scorn which the marbles amateur can draw upon himself.

Usually a team game takes about twenty minutes before a decision is reached, though at the Bearpits I have known a game run to thirty-five minutes. This occasion, I might add, is yet another sad example of how darned wicked they can be at Codgem. It is a tradition in Sussex that marbles must never be played after noon. Once twelve o'clock has struck the tolleys are collected and put in their hiding places for the rest of the day. As a general rule marbles matches start at opening time in the morning and finish about 11.45 a.m., after which everybody retires into the public bar. But one Easter Monday at the Bearpits the Bearbaiters had to face the Marshmallows and there was some consternation because that season the Marshmallows really looked like achieving the impossible – breaking the Bearbaiters' record of never having been defeated on their own beds.

'It maun happen,' said 'Wee Walter' before the game. 'We'll get a liddle light practice first by playing the Artfuls and they ninnies from Ninfield and meet the Marshmallows larst. That ull leave 'em worrying and fretting.'

But 'Wee Walter's' real plan was soon apparent. It was just after 11.25 a.m. when the match with the Marshmallows began. It was a tense struggle and even the cathedral-like hush in which the game was played was broken by occasional hoarse whispers of ' 'ee fudged that un.' 'Fudging', or shooting with the hand over the edge of the bed, is strictly disallowed, and both sides 'fudged' so often that the clock began to take control. I am sure that 'Wee Walter' had urged 'fudging' as deliberate tactics to waste time; in Codiham 'fudging' didn't disqualify a team, it merely meant the shot had to be taken again. Thus, as Saint Mildred's tolled twelve o'clock, 'Wee Walter', with a satanic grin crinkling his beard, bore down on the marbles ring and grabbed the tolleys.

There was 'no result'; Codiham's record had been saved and the Marshmallows thwarted. But if you think that the Marshmallows screamed blue murder and chased round the ring like irate footballers round a referee, you would be mistaken. They glowered silently, shook their heads and went sorrowfully into the public bar to mull over their fate in pints of beer.

'Aren't you going to make a protest?' I asked one Marshmallow.

'It were twelve o'clock all right,' he murmured. 'It were twelve o'clock and it were quite fair to smug 'em.'

'Smugging' is an operation in marbles by which, at the stroke of mid-day, you can perfectly legitimately grab the marbles from the ring and call it quits. Disreputable, perhaps, but in the true tradition of marbles.

10. Trouble at Cucking Green

SPRING, with all the deliberately assumed insouciance of a politician making promises at election time, arrived like a transformation scene in a pantomime that first March we spent in Codiham. One week-end it had been snowing with relentless insistence and the billowing, flying clouds, which the locals call 'messengers', bore tidings of worse to come; then, within forty-eight hours, the wind veered round to south-west and with the thaw came a Corybantic fandango of sunshine that sucked up the moisture so that a sheeny-pile carpet of low-lying mist spread itself across Cucking Green.

Eva snorted that there was 'nothing to get vlothered about' and added that 'fine weather in March is all mizmazing.' It was only townspeople, I learned, who became excited at the first hints of spring. To country folk any heat-wave in March was a subtle plot by nature to mislead all those who worked on the land.

But the heat-wave continued. Under the trees in the garden crocuses gave way to bluebells and wild daffodils and where we had planned a geranium bed mint surprisingly appeared. In the spirit of careless abandon engendered by such carnival antics of plant life and the hearing of the first cynical call of the cuckoo, we all acted out of character. I sang in the bath, Sylvia tangoed by herself round the fruit trees and we both forgot our original vow to have nothing to do with vegetables. Potatoes were planted and lettuce sown – the latter against Eva's awful warnings of frosts to come. But luck was with us; the heat-wave lasted a month.

It was, as the more knowing of the villagers said, 'good cucking weather,' a phrase which, when 'cucking' was pronounced to rhyme with 'cooking', puzzled us somewhat. They merely meant that the combination of warm weather and long, dark evenings was admirably suited to the vernal fevers and venal hopes of Codiham's youth. 'Cucking' never completely ended in the village; there were always a few hardy couples who, finding some gnarled and sheltered oak on the Green, would carry on the traditional sport even at Christmastide. But, as a general custom, 'cucking' was confined to a period lasting from early May until early October.

Late in March that year, however, between the hours of seven and eleven each night, human life stirred stealthily on Cucking Green. There were squeals of girls as well as the hoots of owls, muffled laughter as well as scampering squirrels and the slope of the Cricket Club's outfield became one vast double-bed where it merged into the rhododendron bushes. The whispered, not-so-vehement protests and the wordless, onomatopaeic wood-pigeon cooing of lovers suggested there was much adone-doing as well as do-adoning. Jeans and duffle-coats formed weird silhouettes so that sex was undefinable; crew-cuts and urchin crops huddled together; deep in the undergrowth bottles clinked and corks popped, cigarettes flickered like glow-worms, then flowered into a catherine wheel of sparks as they met in one long Dutch kiss. Night crept over the Green like a rising tide of black ink, mercifully blotting out the ebb and flow of love's liquescent dreams over which the floodlit portrait of Miranda presided like a distant, encouraging beacon.

Even Flossie Whitcombe couldn't remember such 'goings on' on the Green since a Scots regiment was stationed near Codiham during the war. 'They do seem,' she said, 'to 'ave stirred up all they old practices even to 'anging up a girl's garter on a tree. Why, this marning, coming back from Sprogget's, I did count nine such garters all hung on different trees.'

At the risk of being suspected of blackmail, I must confess I often wished I had a tape-recorder with me when I walked around, or across the Green at night. It could have provided a perfect source of documented rustic philanderings. Though there were some snatches of transatlantic jargon, some sneers at 'squares' and praise for 'cats' and 'chicks', it was the ancient language of Sussex which more often stirred youth from its amoristic incoherence into some semblance of articulation. Almost, it seemed, Cupid had put the clock back. This could often be misleading for a Town Clot, for how was I to know that, under the beeches, a 'faggot' was a saucy girl and not a bundle of sticks, that 'Dutch cousins' were plighted lovers, that a 'cockered-up story' was a sample of a suitor's blarney. François L'Amour must have found it all rather disconcerting when Peg told him that he left her 'all mizmazed[1] in my inside.'

'Tis a real dish of tongues[2] I'll get when I get home tonight,' I overheard one wench say. 'You so fanned[3] me about, my clotheses is all torn.'

'If you weren't so crummy,[4] happen they straps and strings wouldn't stretch and snap so,' was the prompt rejoinder.

'It's the trees wot do do things to 'ee. Indoors you be like a mouse, but on the grass you behave like a wild 'orse.'

And on the fringes of the Green, close to the Merry Damsel, two youths were swopping stories of captured garters. 'You can see mine on yonder oak, pinned up inside the 'oller. I never did see such an un as that. A garter with a big scarlet and gold rosette on it in Codiham United colours and that Harrison-Tracey fellow's picture stitched in the centre.'

'Ah, that be Draggle-Tail Dora. She were team's mascot larst winter. She bain't much to look at, but to touch there be not a lass like 'er. Soft and downy like a lamb and as playful as a kitten.'

Nobody minded much about what went on in the dark, but the trouble started when daylight revealed a very wanton Cucking Green, strewn with empty bottles and considerable evidence that the teachings of Dr. Marie Stopes had not been lost on the youthful villagers. The crisis came when one morning a pair of scarlet nylon knickers floated from the top of the Cricket Club's flagstaff.

Club officials, oblivious of the guffaws of youthful spectators, removed the offending article and decided to appoint a watchman to guard against future activities by the 'cuckers'. Dan Budgen, their groundsman, however, interpreted this order rather more intelligently than it had been given; he merely greased the flagstaff and fixed spikes half way up it. That might have been the end of the matter but for the fact that when club members went to inspect the cricket pitch they found it covered with mole-hills. No such catastrophe had occurred within living memory and at an emergency meeting it was decided to organize a series of mole-hunts.

---

[1] Confused.
[2] A scolding.
[3] Teased.
[4] Fat and fleshy.

'We daren't use the mower until we've cleared away every mole-hill,' said Dan.

'And what's more,' replied the parish clerk, ever jealous of Council property, 'the Council will never rent you their mower until we are satisfied it's not going to be damaged by mole-hills.'

The most sensible plan would have been to call in the Codiham Rat and Sparrow Club, but as Jim Bricknell was otherwise employed at the time, this was considered impracticable. Professional mole-catchers are almost extinct today and no member of the Cricket Club had the knowledge of how to locate mole-runs, or how to set traps. They relied entirely on a fork plunged swiftly into moving earth, or on moistened carbide placed in holes in the ground. And, as they soon discovered, mole-hunting without know-how is a slow business when the moon is temporarily obscured by a cloud, and extremely trying to the temper. By the end of a week it was a very harassed party of cricketers who waited, pitch-forks in hand, ready to pounce at the first stirrings of the top-soil. It dawned on all that they might much more profitably be spending their time in the Bearpits, or watching the 'telly'.

One night Bob Peart, Codiham's fast bowler, had been standing motionless, fork in hand, in a corner of the outfield, close to a clump of trees, when he heard a rustling in the grass only a few yards away. Tip-toeing forward, he thrust his fork vigorously into what he hoped was a surfacing mole. The night was dark and it is hard to say who was most surprised – Peart, when he heard a sudden shriek, or the couple whom he had disturbed. A ruffled romeo rose from the ground to grip Peart by the scruff of the neck and accuse him of being a Peeping Tom, actively encouraged by his indignant female companion. Peart recovered his presence of mind sufficiently to launch a counter-attack; other cricketers rushed over to see what was happening and within a few minutes there was a free-for-all on the Green. 'Cuckers' appeared from the hollows of trees and the denser parts of the undergrowth, confronted the cricketers and hurled clods of earth at them. The cricketers, bewildered and angry, charged with pitch-forks which gave them an unfair advantage in the rout which ensued.

But if the cricketers won the battle that night, the 'cuckers' reversed the result the following evening, when, reinforced by a posse of Teddy Boys from Henty, armed with catapults and hoses, they drove their adversaries back to the cricket pavilion and inflicted several severe, if not very serious injuries.

The committee of the Cricket Club sent a deputation to the Parish

Council, asking for drastic steps to be taken to deal with 'hooliganism and vandalism' and soon the village was divided into pro-Cricket Club and pro-'cucking' factions. This cut across all normal alliances, for, though the Cricket Club had powerful allies both on the Parish Council and among residents of the Green, many took the view that the Green was a sanctuary for all and that cricketers had no business there except on Saturday afternoons and Bank Holidays in summer-time.

The battle was resumed in the Parish Council chamber. Colonel Skinner, as president of the Cricket Club, led the assault on the 'cuckers' as though once again he was back in the Punjab campaigning. With clipped, martial phrases he denounced them as 'these devlish delinquents, this, this . . . adolescent riff-raff.'

This brought Councillor Miss Ablethorpe to the rescue of the 'cuckers'. No one would have accused the prim Miss Ablethorpe of ever having indulged in 'cucking', but she sternly rebuked the Colonel for his 'unseemly and unbridled language' and, tartly reminding him that moral welfare was her particular preserve, pointed out that he was not 'Codiham born and bred as *I* am and therefore unqualified to pass judgment on our youth.'

'I can form my own opinion, madam,' replied the Colonel. 'If I had my way, I would ban them from the Green altogether. What we want is a police patrol on the Green. A few salutary prosecutions and we'd soon clear up this sort of trouble.'

'You are not in the Punjab now, Colonel,' quietly observed Miss Ablethorpe, who had more patience with missionaries than the military.

This gave Jonathan Heggy, the Parish Council's one and only Socialist, just the opening he had hoped for. 'No,' he thundered back, 'the Colonel is not in the Punjab any more. And what's more Codgem is not the Punjab. It's the likes of you who want to bring fascism to Codgem. You want to turn our village into a police state.'

'Withdraw! Withdraw!' shouted the Colonel.

'I'll withdraw nothing,' retorted Jonathan. 'I know what the Colonel has in mind. But what did he do when I asked the Council to build a social centre for our teenagers? He said we couldn't afford it. Now he wants it both ways – to drive our teenagers out of doors and to get the police to whip 'em into cells.'

'I said nothing about cells. I—'

'Now, gentlemen,' said Dick Pride, always one for compromise whether on price, or policy, 'don't let us get all vlothered about a bit of yostering[1]

---

[1] Behaving noisily or roughly.

on the Green. There's room for all parties on Cucking Green, if they behave themselves, and I don't doubt but what there are two sides to this story. If anyone has complaints, if anyone has been injured, or had property damaged, let him go to the police. But I don't think we want to send the police out looking for trouble. I doubt if we have the powers.'

'The by-laws of the Green do permit us to take action,' primly interposed the parish clerk, thumbing the pages of a book. 'There is Article seventeen, sub-section b, which clearly states. . .'

'I move we go into committee,' urged Harry Sprogget. 'There are certain things which might more freely be discussed behind closed doors. We don't want the whole village to know we are dis-united on so serious a matter.'

'I'll oppose that,' stormed Jonathan. 'I'm dead against secret sessions. They only serve those with vested interests,' he added darkly, obviously hinting at Sprogget & Sons.

'I resent that remark,' cracked back Harry. 'At least I don't seek cheap support from Teddy Boys.'

'No more do I,' barked Jonathan. 'And wot's more there aren't any Teddy Boys in Codgem. The trouble-makers come from Henty.'

'I was about to second Councillor Sprogget's motion that we go into committee, when I was so rudely interrupted by Councillor Heggy,' piped up Mr. Sosserthwaite, a newcomer to the Council who was none other than that stockbroker-farmer to whom Eva had taken so strong a dislike.

Harry Sprogget looked uneasy at this unwanted support for his motion, for Mr. Sosserthwaite was disliked by a majority of the Parish Council. Not only was he a 'furriner', but it was whispered that he had used undue influence to persuade a potential opponent to stand down and so allow him to be elected unopposed to the Council. He had no real roots in Codiham except for a farm on which he showed a handsome loss to the Inland Revenue inspector. Not only was he suspected of farming merely to dodge paying his full amount of tax, but of surreptitiously buying up shooting rights in the neighbourhood and aspiring to become a Justice of the Peace.

To be fair to Colonel Skinner, he detested humbug. He might think the younger generation was carousing down the path to ruin, but he was damned if he would stand for that upstart Sosserthwaite gabbling about going into committee when all he really cared about was the market value of his own property on the Green.

'I oppose the motion,' he snapped. 'This isn't a matter of hush-hush talk, but of decency and good citizenship. I'm not going to be a party to any touting of financial interests behind closed doors.'

'That is very unwise talk, Colonel. I said nothing about financial interests. The value of all our property on the Green is something far transcending mere financial interest.'

'Balderdash, man!' expostulated Colonel Skinner.

'Good for you, Colonel,' put in Jonathan unexpectedly. 'I'm with you there. No secret sessions.'

By now the issues were so confused that it was impossible to tell who was on which side. Harry Sprogget, embarrassed at the idea of clashing with a customer as valuable as Colonel Skinner, apologetically offered to withdraw his motion: 'I have no ulterior motive in this matter. I just felt that there were certain rather – er – delicate matters which were best ventilated in committee.'

'Well, speak out, Councillor Sprogget,' urged Miss Ablethorpe. 'I'm a J.P., you know, and I've probably listened to a good deal of indelicacy on the Bench, not to mention my work in connexion with the Diocesan Moral Welfare Society.'

'My God, yes, I bet she has,' whispered Colonel Skinner to Dick Pride. 'Stayed for three hours listening to that incest case at Henty.'

'Well, indeed, ma'am,' began Harry Sprogget, 'I do not doubt that we are all men and women – or perhaps I should say, ladies – of the world. I only trust that what I have to say will not seem too outrageous in open Council. Really all I had in mind was to raise the matter of Cucking Pond.'

'Cucking Pond, Councillor Sprogget? And what has that got to do with the subject?' boomed Miss Ablethorpe, who delighted in teasing the Grocer Extraordinary.

'Quite a lot, ma'am, I fear. Not since my father's day have I heard rumours of black magic on Cucking Green, but I very much regret to say that something of the sort is going on there these nights. And I think the Parish Clerk will agree we could take steps about that.'

There was a buzz of surprised exclamations. Mr. Sosserthwaite permitted himself a wry and patronizing smile while he patted his thin moustache. Colonel Skinner, who could never resist making the feeblest of jokes, grunted something about 'old Sprogget must have found one of his own Black Magic chocolate boxes on the Green'.

'The other night,' continued Harry Sprogget, 'I was taking my dog for a run near the Pond rather later than usual. I had been up late doing my accounts, otherwise I shouldn't have been abroad at such an hour. It must have been about eleven-thirty. There was laughing and splashing going on in the Pond and naturally I peeped through the trees to see what was going on. What I saw appeared to be some strange kind of ritual. There was a youth and a girl, standing in bathing costumes waist deep at the edge of the Pond while another youth was reading something out of a book. There was a lot of talk about "bit necks" and something about "sacrificing this chick to this cat" and after that a lot of singing of some very rude words to the tune of Handel's Wedding March. I can only assume that these young people were practising some black-magic rite and sacrificing a live chicken and a cat.'

It was left to Miss Ablethorpe, that doughty and, one would have thought, serenely sheltered spinster, to explain to Harry and a bewildered Council the full significance of what the grocer had seen and heard.

'I am very glad that Councillor Sprogget has raised this matter in Council so that it is now possible to put the whole subject in its proper perspective,' she said. 'It would be wholly undesirable to have rumours of witchcraft and black magic going around the village, probably bringing hordes of newspaper reporters descending on us from London.

'What you saw and heard, Councillor Sprogget, was, in fact, very different from what you imagined it to be. Far from being black magic, it was merely a rustic manifestation of a pecular sect of young people mainly associated with the United States and sometimes heard of in the purlieus of Bloomsbury and Chelsea.

'As you all know, I have made a study of moral welfare and my work has taken me among some very peculiar people indeed. Councillor Sprogget spoke of "bit necks". This may sound rather frightening, but undoubtedly the word he heard mentioned was Beatniks.'

'Beatniks?' inquired Harry. 'What on earth are they?'

'A Beatnik,' replied Miss Ablethorpe in much the same self-confident manner she adopted when lecturing to the Women's Institute on juvenile delinquency, her favourite theme, 'a Beatnik is an abbreviation of "beatific". It is a way of life among certain young people who describe themselves as "Holy Barbarians". The Beatnik considers himself, or herself, rather a cut above the rest, despising money and power and usually wearing old clothes rather as a kind of uniform.'

'Most extraordinary,' said Colonel Skinner. 'Do you mean to say we have Beatniks in Codiham?'

'So it would seem. I should imagine that some of the younger artists who have seen Beatnikism in London, Paris and possibly New York, have introduced the idea to some of our less literate and more irresponsible village youth. Quite deplorable, but we must face facts.'

'But this ritual I saw and the queer words they used? Is this a kind of Beatnik language?' asked Harry.

'Beatniks do speak a rather meaningless jargon, mostly monosyllabic and abbreviated. For example, they will keep silent for many minutes and then say "Drop".'

'Drop? Drop what?' demanded Colonel Skinner.

'Drop dead, Colonel.'

'I beg your pardon, ma'am.'

'I was not being personal, I was merely giving an example of how Beatniks talk.'

'Isn't this all rather a waste of time?' interpolated Mr. Sosserthwaite. 'Aren't we getting away from the subject?'

'The Council may judge that when I have finished speaking,' icily replied Miss Ablethorpe. 'The Beatnik wears, as I said, old clothes, and hideous woollen stockings, usually black, red or green, sometimes blue. The male Beatnik does not cut his hair and the female makes her face up in a revoltingly ugly travesty of what Nature intended it to be. The men are referred to as "cats" and the girls as "chicks". That is what you heard, Councillor Sprogget. It was nothing to do with black magic, or sacrifice. They also have their own private, mock marriages, usually conducted, so I understand, at night and in the sea. Presumably Cucking Pond was a natural substitute.'

.   .   .   .   .

The county newspapers were full of the Parish Council debate on Cucking Green. Indeed, the Press generally took the keenest interest in the revelations of Councillor Sprogget and Miss Ablethorpe's dissertation on Beatniks. 'Are there Beatniks in Codiham?' asked one headline. 'Black Magic or Beatnikism?' stated another. The national Press sent men down to interview Harry Sprogget and some of the teenagers, and a village girl who proudly proclaimed 'I'm a Beatnik' appeared on television programmes after a cameraman had scoured the neighbourhood in search of talent. But with the threat of unwelcome publicity from outside, Codiham closed its ranks and the warring factions had second thoughts. Even the few hooligans from Henty were angry with the Beatniks, fearing they would be blamed for the activities of these 'bloody eggheads'. Colonel Skinner invited Jonathan Heggy to a drink in the

Merry Damsel to seek a compromise, having been urged to do so by Dick Pride.

'Sorry, Jonathan, m'boy,' said old Skinner. 'Perhaps I did rather over-do the police stuff. After all, I was a young blood m'self once. Ha! Ha! Remember kissing a wench in the bracken near Bagshot in my Sandhurst days.'

'Perhaps I said more'n I should, too, Colonel,' agreed Jonathan. 'Anyhow, I'm damned glad you put that sausage-face Sosserthwaite in his place. The blasted capitalist!'

'Well, Jonathan, you can't accuse me of being that, dammit. Lost all m'money in Malayan rubber years ago. Just living on m' pension and drinking beer instead of Scotch these days.'

'That's what you all say. Main thing is we got to do summat about Sosserthwaite.'

'I think we'll persuade the doctor to stand for election next year. Mind you, he's a bit of a crank, believes in all this psychiatric nonsense, but he has the good of the village at heart and Sosserthwaite won't stand a chance against him. But if I back you there, Jonathan, don't you go making political propaganda out of this Green affair. We must stamp out this hooliganism and this Beatnik nonsense. Bless my soul, the things that Miss Ablethorpe knows. Beatnik weddings, eh? Can't have that Yankee flim-flam in this village. And no pitched battles either.'

'I teckon as 'ow these Beatniks is quite 'armless. Just a bit of fun, though it do seem as 'ow it ain't very wholesome fun. The real trouble-makers all come from Henty. And the danger night is Thursday because that's when the Henty boys come over here. Now if we arranged to have a police patrol – not on the Green, mark you – each Thursday night in the vicinity of the Green, on the roadway, so to speak, I think we could check the trouble.'

'Well, that's a step in the direction of common sense, though I must say I don't think one police officer will be enough. The devil of it is, Jonathan, the real trouble-maker in this affair is Sosserthwaite. Do you know what he wants? His whole idea of going into committee was to persuade us to fence off the Green, make it into a park and lock it up at night. Then I'd have to walk right round the Green instead of crossing it when I left the Merry Damsel. And, mark you, Jonathan, though I'm all for stern discipline and teaching these Teddy Boys what's what, I don't believe in monkeying with the freedom of the individual any more than you. Why the devil shouldn't the boys and girls have a bit of slap and tickle, if they wish, as long as they keep discreet, and don't hold these dam' fool mock weddings?'

Thus did the forthright Colonel and the Socialist firebrand bridge the gap which lay between their points of view. It wasn't so big a gap really and, when 'furriners' like Mr. Sosserthwaite were rampant, it was a case of presenting a United Village Front. Jonathan, with memories of Popular Fronts to cheer him up, thought this was a splendid slogan. When Sosserthwaite proposed a curfew for the Green at the next Parish Council meeting, he was outvoted ten to one. Police-constable Nottidge, suitably briefed, did a little quiet detective work on his own and showed remarkable common sense in dealing with the offenders. Within a few weeks 'cucking' had resumed its traditional, unobtrusive style and Beatnikism had disappeared as an alien, unCodgemite way of life.

I asked Nottidge how he managed to achieve these results. 'I just warned the Henty boys that I'd pick 'em up if there was any more nonsense,' he replied, 'and I hinted to the others that if they didn't behave them-selves, old Sosserthwaite ud close the Green of a night. And between you and me, that did the trick. There was all that talk of nude bathing after the "Bit Necks" wedding. I told the parish clerk the way to stop that. "Put some more swans on the Pond," I said. "That ull larn 'em."'

The Cricket Club mole-hunters completed their round-up and by the time the season started Dan Budgen with loving care and fussing pride had once again prepared an unbelievably good wicket, even if the ball tended to play strange tricks at the pavilion end. From my study window I had the good fortune to see the batsman at the pavilion end. When Bob Peart was bowling there was always plenty of fun.

Bob's aim was the suspect spot at the pavilion end. If he found this in his first over, he was almost unplayable and wickets crashed like ninepins. He made a long, swinging run, dragging his huge feet like a carthorse, but, despite his clumsy action, he was really fast and could make the ball develop the kick of a mule when it struck the spot. Then, either the batsman took a resounding smack on the chest, or he played a half-hearted defensive stroke and cocked up a dolly catch to the doctor at silly mid-on.

Bob Peart was feared for miles around; he even terrorized some opponents into playing him with a pad between chest and sweater. Yet he was easily upset and, if he failed to find his cherished spot, or to take a wicket in the first few overs, began temperamentally serving up full tosses which were treated with scant respect once the batsman had regained his nerve. This, in effect, meant that I either saw wickets tumbling in rapid succession, or a powerful series of joyous clouts into the rhododendron bushes.

Village cricket may not have the same romantic attractions which invested it fifty years ago, but it has a magnetism which all save a few county sides have long since lost. If, half an hour before stumps were drawn, the scoreboard told me that Codiham had to make forty to win with four wickets to fall, it was always a temptation to push away the typewriter and make for the Green. All the village seemed to have the same idea at such moments. As if by telepathy, news of the scoreboard's tale would percolate to the Bearpits and the Merry Damsel, to the cottages in Silk Lane and the shops around the Green. A steady procession of villagers, male and female, would suddenly develop a fast, jerky, animated gait; it was as though a film of the Green had been taken by a cameraman of the silent screen era and that this had been projected on to a screen at treble the normal pace. Walking far more quickly than was their custom, they took up positions on the boundary line and under the trees. And, even if play flagged, there was the conversation to entertain one. It is extraordinary what a wealth of shrewd judgment and carefully chosen phrases makes up the spontaneous commentary of your village cricket spectator, especially in a county like Sussex where there is always someone who remembers seeing 'Ranji' making a feathered leg-glance, or watching Maurice Tate bowling an immaculate length all day long and never wavering.

'It ud do Bob Peart good to 'ave seen Maurice Tate. There were one who'd give 'im a lesson. They doan't come that way nowadays. Why, Tate ud keep his length like a nun keeping her virginity.'

Such comparisons may have been grossly unfair, but, allowing for this, most of the older spectators talked sound cricket sense.

'Tich and run, Vicar!' they would shout to Martyn Bowker who was devoted to snatching chancy singles and usually got himself run out in the process. 'Tich and run. But doan't 'ee do it if the ball goes near point. 'Ee's a deadly hand at throwin' in.'

Of course, in Codiham, as on most village grounds, there are 'none as good as the old uns' in the opinion of the veteran critics. They make one exception in favour of Sir Oswald Thyme, who, in their view, 'can hit 'em as hard as they come'. Alas, Sir Oswald only plays for the first two matches of Cricket Week. For Codiham is unique in its methods of team selection. Not being so fanatical about winning matches as either the Football Club, or the Bearbaiters' Marbles Team, the Codiham cricket tradition is to give every member of the club a chance to play.

To achieve this a strict roster of players is kept so that each gets a turn and it is almost an unwritten rule that the Vicar turns out for his annual game on Whit Monday.

I find it a little hard to credit the accuracy of all the spectators. There is one old man who never ceases to insist that he once saw the great Alfred Mynn catch a swallow in full flight on Cucking Green. 'And 'ee asked the umpire "Azzat?" and the umpire gave the batsman out.'

This story, which has also been told of Percy Chapman and Gilbert Jessop, is spoiled by the fact that Alfred Mynn died in 1861.

11. Parson's fishing rights

An early caller at the Oast House was the Vicar. This may seem quite normal practice to the initiated, but to us, accustomed to urban seclusion, it was something for which we hadn't bargained.

Now, devoted as we may seem to be to wickedness in its more artistic manifestations, we have, a little illogically, perhaps, always felt that life without a church is no sort of a life at all. You may say that this is some deep-rooted conviction that a church is a sanctuary for sinners. It is one of those subjects on which it is difficult to draw a Plimsoll line to divide a false sentimentality from a too stern regard for intellectual rectitude. As soon as one begins to set down such thoughts on paper, especially in the context of a Wicked Village, it isn't easy to define where Dr. Jekyll McCormick ends and Mr. Hyde McCormick raises his glass.

If the Monster Hyde leers over a pint in the Hole, or casts an acquisitively approving eye at Maisie's elegant calf and trim little buttocks as she crosses the Green, you must also accept that Jekyll occasionally attends a service at Saint Mildred's. You may deduce that I do so for snobbish reasons, or to appease the vicar, or because it isn't opening time until the service is over. I don't propose to argue about it. All I can say is that, as a family, we do sometimes say 'Let's go to church' in rather the same way one might suggest 'Let's have one at the Damsel.' Shocking perhaps, and yet—

I do not believe that any civilized community can avoid decadence without having a church as a rallying point. I agree that many civilized communities have become decadent in spite of such possessions and sometimes even because of them. There are, of course, individuals of great integrity and philosophical strength of purpose, who can survive morally unscathed without acknowledging a church. But they are far fewer in number than they egotistically believe.

I must also admit that I don't say 'Let's go to the Friends' Meeting House, or the Methodist Chapel' – the two other places of worship in Codiham. Yet, on balance, I have no doubt that the congregations at both these places are more deserving of the title of 'practising Christians' than the worshippers at Saint Mildred's. In fact, the vicar has even admitted as much to me over a glass of sherry. But that is as it should be: the Friends and the Methodists developed as an antidote to eighteenth-century wickedness in the village, ever since John Wesley came here to preach against smuggling and was pelted with stones for his rashness.

Ethics and common sense tell me that the Friends are much nearer to a state of absolute religious integrity than the rank and file of the Church of England. On the other hand any nonconformist attitude seems far too rigid, too anxious to equate worship with austerity, to make any headway in the twentieth century. There is something lochetic about the harsh brickwork of the Methodist Chapel and the unlovely windows; I never pass this building without feeling that it is inhabited by a teetotal ogre lying in wait for me and somehow, though in the village, it never seems a part of it like Saint Mildred's.

Saint Mildred's, like so many other churches of the Anglican faith, survives partly because of its intrinsic beauty and partly because the Church of England, whatever its many historical faults, preserves sufficient elasticity to give us now a Wilberforce, now a Temple, a Dick Sheppard and a Canon Collins, a Conrad Noel and a Canon Rhodes, or even a delightful old Marxist like the Dean of Canterbury.

The chap who openly brags he never goes into a church and who remains unmoved when he sees so enchanting a place of worship as Saint Mildred's is probably a dull dog. You may say with Karl Marx that religion is the opiate of the people. It can be and opiates can also be prescribed for sick people. A civilization (so-called) that can kid itself, or be kidded, that it has 'never had it so good' while working all week and spending its Sundays laying the new crazy paving, or painting the house, has become such a work-drugged community that a little religious opiate might not be a bad thing.

All this is far remote from the vicar who could, I assure you, sum up the position much better than I. I am, if you like, one of the marginal church-goers, the sinner with a foot in both camps, whose positive vote has yet to be captured. And for this reason I rather dreaded a call from the Vicar of Codiham; it was a little too reminiscent of a canvassing politician. I feared he might be a hearty bore who would chortle and incite to evangelical fervour, with a mixture of *bonhomie* and over-powering persuasion. Or he might be a stern cleric who would call, shake his head in sorrow and forever after cast reproving and castigatory glances at me when I entered the Merry Damsel.

In London one didn't have such problems. In the country, I feared, one either went to church regularly, or one didn't go at all. There was no half-measure. And it was a half-measure I wanted, or rather a liqueur-glassful of church-going, when the mood took one, and a tumbler of well-watered Strindbergian scepticism.

I need not have worried. When Martyn Bowker called I was pounding a typewriter. My wife was rash enough to mention to him that I was an author, which must have made him expect to see a horned monster appear. Instead of which he greeted me with an apologetic laugh and introduced himself. . . .

'I'm Martyn Bowker, your vicar. I hear you're a writer like myself. Only I write sermons which no one would print and you publish sermons which somebody will buy.'

'I wouldn't put it quite like that,' I said cautiously, fearing that he might be after a subscription for something or other. 'Unless you feel that the truth as I see it is a sermon.'

'We've all got sermons in us,' continued the vicar. 'Look at Dorothy Sayers. She kept them all locked up inside her while she was writing all her Peter Wimsey stories. However, I haven't come to talk about sermons. Please regard this as purely a personal call – just to say hello. After all, you live in the shadows of my church, as it were, and it would be most unneighbourly if I didn't call. How did you come to find this oast house?'

I told him of my chance visit to Codiham and the meeting with 'Sailor' Thompsett.

'Ah, yes, that's so like Thompsett. Always willing to help. A splendid fellow really. A buccaneering, bluff, frank fellow. Know where you stand with him. And I might tell you that though he has a most disreputable fund of stories, though he hasn't been inside Saint Mildred's since he was a boy, he knows the Bible better than anyone else in this parish.'

' "Sailor" knows his Bible?'

'Yes, indeed. When I first came to Codiham I decided to try and reform "Sailor". Very foolish of me because in the eyes of God I doubt if "Sailor" needs much reforming. His wickedness is the wickedness of a naughty boy and there's not a lot you can do about it. I even went round to the Bearpits some nights to have a beer with him, but he quoted the Bible back at me every time I tried to find any fault with his conduct.

'I was young and *gauche* then, but I learned my lesson. I can laugh at my clumsiness now. I was telling "Sailor" about the divine commands to Moses and I dare say I was being rather priggish. "Ah, yes, Vicar," said "Sailor", "the Lord saith unto Moses 'Come forth' all right. And what happened? He came fifth and lost the job."

'But I soon came to see how very easily we in the Church can fail to realize how gold and dross are inexplicably mixed up.'

.   .   .   .   .

There are, of course, still many villages where aged vicars intone drearily and unmelodiously and preach sermons which have little bearing on the age we live in. In Southern England they can get away with it – even a lazy clergyman who preaches the same poor sermon three times a year to the same congregation. In Nonconformist Wales and parts of Devon and Cornwall they are much more concerned with the merits of the preacher than the form of the service and a bad preacher usually loses his congregation to another church or chapel. But a quiet, almost imperceptible revolution is coming in the Church of England and the unworldly, drawing-room clergyman of fiction has disappeared just as the fox-hunting Lord of the Manor-dominated, crusty old reactionary vicar dissolved into oblivion with the First World War. Martyn Bowker is in many ways typical of the new spirit among the clergy and he has succeeded in breaking down the gulf that has too long existed between those who go to Church regularly and those who never go at all.

He frankly admits (in confidence, of course, and not arrogantly) that he would willingly exchange some of his church members for some of those who never attend a church at all. No names from the vicar, but I feel sure he has Mr. Sosserthwaite in mind. There is no doubt that Sosserthwaite regards the vicar as a 'dangerous thinker', a man with unsound views on the H-bomb, take-over bids and racial questions. This may suggest that Martyn Bowker is a politically-minded clergyman, but this is not so. No one knows better than he that a village church is not the place to preach politics and it is only in the parish magazine that he permits himself to touch on such topics and even then with carefully measured words. 'The parish magazines gets into the pubs,' he told me, 'for I drop them in there myself. And, who knows, I may be an optimist, but I always hope that somebody, picking up a copy, may start an argument on what I've written. If they'll talk on these things in the pubs, so much the better.'

No sooner had the Cucking Green controversy died down than Codiham was suddenly confronted with the spectacle of its vicar doing battle like 'Some village Hampden that, with dauntless breast, the little tyrant of his field withstood.' This was the issue of the Parson's Fishing Rights which brought the vicar into a staunch alliance with 'Sailor' Thompsett, so it would seem that their early meetings in the Bearpits had not been in vain.

For centuries it had been the unchallenged right of any vicar of Codiham to take fish from the wattle fish-trap which stretched like a screen across the junction of the River Dentical and Parson's Pond. This was known as the Parson's Catch, taken on the first tides after the new and full moons, granted by the fishermen of bygone days who thought it more sensible if the vicar caught his own fish instead of receiving the fish-tithe of one-tenth of every catch made. The monks of Westhurst Abbey had laid the foundations of this tradition. They built the fish-trap and throughout the centuries, without objections from any quarter, vicars of Codiham had enjoyed this privilege.

Now this privilege was threatened by the formidable combination of Mr. Sosserthwaite, who owned a good deal of the land bordering Parson's Pond, and the Dentical Catchment Board. I suspect that the former had suggested to the latter that the vicar was usurping their rights and, unhappily, bureaucracy is often far more vigilant about its own rights than is the individual about his. So the Catchment Board arbitrarily took over the wattle fish-trap and, having tasted the delights of confiscation, took just one step too many by claiming mooring fees from some of the few fishermen who still lived in Codiham. This led to a protest meeting by the fishermen at the Hole in the Wall, for under an ancient by-law it was clearly laid down that

'We will enjoin and command ye that all and singular Men and Tenants of the Manor of Codiham aforesaid be permitted to be exempt from homage or payment of mooring fees, of tolls, pannage, murrage or other things for carriage passing of goods or any other thing on the River Dentical or waters of which the said river has its source.'

Two hundred years ago, when the quay alongside the Hole in the Wall was in constant use, the right of free moorings on the Dentical was of the utmost importance to the fishermen of Codiham. With the silting up of the river and the consequent falling into disuse of the quay, fishing had become of less importance and not only were there very few fishermen left, but those remaining were either pensioners, who only fished occasionally, or men who fished as a side-line and relied mainly on other employment.

The Catchment Board argued that, technically, these men weren't any longer fishermen, but motor mechanics, carpenters or labourers. The ancient rights, they claimed, were anomalous and some of the so-called fishermen had very doubtful claims to being 'men and tenants of the Manor of Codiham'.

One morning the Reverend Martyn Bowker took me over to Parson's Pond and pointed out a thin line across the entrance of the Dentical, following the tell-tale ridge of waves creaming over some hidden obstruction.

'That,' he said, 'is what all the fuss is about. What happens is that, as the tide comes in, a grill in the fish-trap opens and the fish swim into the pond. The receding tide closes the grill and the fish are trapped. All you do then is to walk out and hit them on the head with something heavy. In principle this fish-trap is a combination of the baulk-trap used in some estuaries and the Keddle net fishing system which used to be employed between Lydd and Rye Harbour. There is a complicated arrangement of posts with nets between them. You know the expression "a pretty kettle of fish"? Well, it really should be "a pretty keddle of fish" and refers, of course, to the remarkable variety of catches you can get. "Sailor" Thompsett tells me they once caught a seal in the trap, though that may be a typical fisherman's story.'

The Catchment Board and Mr. Sosserthwaite, though for varying reasons, regarded the fish-trap as a menace to fishing and both wanted to demolish it. However, not even modern bureaucracy could do this without the vicar's consent as the fish-trap was quite legal provided that it was operated by a 'privileged person', the vicar coming within this category by ancient custom.

'I don't deny that this is more of an ancient custom than a law, but then laws are built upon ancient customs,' said Martyn Bowker. 'The

Catchment Board suggest I should surrender my rights and accept some small compensation from them. You may say this is a small matter and that I might as well accept with good grace. But it is an infringement of a vicar's rights and, if relinquished, can only lead to further encroachment by the Catchment Board and other local authorities on other ancient rights such as the fishermen's claims to free moorings.

'Originally the idea was for the fish to supplement the vicar's income. Of course. that doesn't mean much today. I don't catch very much and sometimes I give away my catches, or eat them, or sell them in aid of Church funds. I am holding out against the Board and Mr. Sosserthwaite because I think the historical principle is more important than the monetary value of the catches.

'Sosserthwaite, who wants the fishing rights all to himself, says that the trap is a form of poaching. But this is nonsense. It doesn't interfere with anyone's fishing because the trap catches the fish as they come from the river into the sea and not as they swim up the river. This way the church benefits from what small sales there are and the people get fish far cheaper than they would otherwise. And if the fishermen don't object, why should the Catchment Board?'

The fishermen not only supported the vicar's rights, but offered to give evidence on his behalf. Mainly through 'Sailor' Thompsett's intervention the Association of the Fishermen of Codiham was formed to fight for their free mooring rights. And, arguing that, technically, the vicar was also a 'Fishermen of Codiham', they unanimously elected him president of the Assocation.

The battle is still going on and its echoes may be heard from time to time. The vicar insists on retaining the fish-trap and the Association claims that they, and not the Catchment Board, should be responsible for operating it. Mr. Sosserthwaite took the matter to the High Court and sought to compel the vicar to surrender his rights. He lost his case. Meanwhile, the Catchment Board is at loggerheads with Codiham Parish Council on the question of mooring fees. But there is no doubt that the village as a whole considers this a supreme issue of individual freedom.

.   .   .   .   .

Martyn Bowker's enthusiasm for bell-ringing has already been mentioned. A lover of detective stories, he always said that his greatest debt to Dorothy Sayers was that *The Nine Tailors* so fascinated him that he took up campanology as a hobby. 'I have cut out from her book that splendid thought of hers: "in an age of loud noises, bell ringing is the only one made to the glory of God." It is framed in my study together with photographs of the inscription on each of our bells.'

The bells of Saint Mildred's are, after her spire and tower, incomparably her finest possession. Their eight tintinnabulating voices lend unity to a variety of emotions: the first, meek enough to inherit the earth, with its sweet-toned treble; the second, arrogant and challenging; the third, the 'death watch bell' as some Codgemites call it; number four, all its seventeen hundred-weights, which only the blacksmith rings; the fifth, proud and martial; the sixth, slightly cracked, and sounding a note of anxiety; and the seventh and eighth, which are the vicar's favourites, because 'on these alone you can effectively ring Stedmans and complicated Surprises.'

In the infinite complexity of their changes the bells provide a thousand sermons which all seem to add up to the simple fact that God and Beauty are one and the same abstraction. Somehow they make an admirable compromise between the artificial dogmas of the Church of England and the enthusiastic romanticism of the Christians before the Dark Ages, between the pagan artist and the ascetic moralist, between Codiham's wickedness and the innate conservatism of the villagers. Beauty, like God, moves in a mysterious way so that it often seems (and never more so than when the bells are ringing) that God masquerades as Beauty. This divine manifestation may be but the arrangement of a line here and a curve there; a splash of scarlet and a daub of grey; the invisible circles of harmonious colours in a picture by Pissarro; the twisting of a phrase in a delicate lyric; all these technicalities are the strange, impersonal, one might almost say unfeeling, laws of Beauty. When we look upon the 'universal blank of nature's works', Beauty appears to be a harsh, immobile sphinx. And it is just the same with God, if you try to give him a mask and fail to see his works.

Martyn Bowker has certainly made the best of Codiham's supreme example of divinely-inspired works – the eight bells. Under his guidance there has been no lack of bellringers. Just before the last war bellringing seemed doomed; the old-time bellringer was dying out. Nobody had the common sense to make youth interested in bells. Today many vicars have achieved this and Martyn Bowker has a reserve team of boy and girl ringers, several only in their early teens. On a summer's afternoon you can see them riding out of the village on their bicycles, the bells of their machines jangling merrily as though to remind everybody of their vocation. This is the occasion of their annual bellringing tour which they have made each year since 1955. For a whole week they pedal across Kent, Sussex and Hampshire, stopping at more than twenty churches where there are bells to ring.

This annual pilgrimage was entirely the vicar's idea and it not only gives his youthful ringers an original holiday (each year they seek out new churches), but enables many peals of bells, which would otherwise now be permanently silent, to give out their inspiriting messages once more.

'It was not always so easy to find bellringers in Codiham,' says the vicar. 'Between the wars nobody seemed to care very much. Indeed, I am told that at Christmas, nineteen-hundred-and-forty-six, the eight bellringers went on strike because the vicar insisted they must also attend divine service. I make no such stipulation. All I do insist on is a reasonably high standard of conduct and attendance at Christmas, Easter and Whitsun. But most of my boys and girls do attend fairly regularly.

'My churchwardens are sometimes a little shocked at youth's choice of tunes at practices. There was the *Harry Lime Theme* I told you about one Guy Fawkes Night. But the bonfire on Cucking Green on November the fifth is always an occasion of celebration at Codiham and, if the village has a torchlight procession, I see no reason why the Church shouldn't join in the fun. But one night after practice an irate Miss Ablethorpe called on me to protest against the playing of *Put Another Nickel In*. My only excuse was that I hadn't recognized the tune.'

I often go to the church during practice sessions and have in consequence learned to understand much of the fascination of campanology for young and old alike. To ring a complete peal takes more than three hours. One mistake ruins it. To make a peal, bells are rung in continually changing order without one repetition. It's not just a matter of pulling a rope. Strength is required less than a good sense of timing and rope sighting, knowing which rope of the other seven or eight to pull immediately after the 'change'.

A 'change' is an alteration in the order in which a given number of bells are rung. The world record is held by a team which rang the St. Lawrence Church bells at Appleton through 21,363 changes in twelve and a half hours, without food or drink. It is possible to get slightly more than 40,000 changes on the eight bells of an average belfry. No ringer can remember all the changes. They have graph-like tables and each ringer is allotted a bell. Anyone who cares to clamber up the narrow, spiralling ladder to the belfry of Saint Mildred's, ignoring the enormous spiders that inhabit it, may see in the dim light from the belfry louvres the framed records of former bellringing feats.

Down at the Hole the vicar is known as 'Belfry Bowker', a nickname of which he is quite proud. He is still a bachelor, though, he adds with a wan smile, 'Like Barkis, "I'm willin'," but the economic facts of a country vicar's life hardly offer much prospect for matrimony. In some ways it is an asset to be a bachelor in a country parish. It ensures one a ready band of lady workers, for the ladies always assume that a bachelor vicar is helpless and needs rallying around. And it does mean I can give a lot more time to things that ought to be done, but which the married clergyman with a family cannot possibly cope with these days when he has to tackle household chores as well. But the vicarage is too large for me. Some day I really will have to settle down and marry.'

'And what type do you think would make the best vicar's wife today?' Sylvia asked him.

'It's not today we have to think of, but tomorrow,' he replied. 'In a really modern church you must have a really modern wife. Modern, mind you, not modish. Preferably classless. It's far more important for the woman to be classless than the man. I have often thought that the very best type of barmaid might make an excellent vicar's wife.'

'How exciting!' exclaimed Sylvia. 'Have you one in mind?'

'Not yet. I'm afraid Flossie Whitcombe might be a little too overpowering,' he laughed. 'But you see, a barmaid, at least the best type of barmaid, deals in souls, too. She sees and understands human nature. She has to be tolerant, a good listener and impervious to all manner of temptations without seeming a prude. So does a vicar's wife.'

'Vicar,' I said, 'I do believe that you, too, feel "us be proper wicked down at Codgem". You really do know the way to their wicked hearts.'

'Joking apart,' he added, looking suddenly serious, 'I have been thinking a lot lately about marriage and friendship. Not for myself, but for the youth. This Cucking Green brouhaha led up to it. I am toying with the idea of a Lonely Hearts' Club in the village. Perhaps it sounds a bit old-maidish, but something ought to be done. It has always seemed to me to be wrong for marriage to be more or less a matter of accident. No one wants to go back to the ancient habit, still current on the Continent, of parents arranging marriages. Yet surely this is quite as good as, if not better than, our modern habit of marriage by chance meeting.

'Everyone thinks that marriage bureaux, Lonely Hearts' Clubs and the like are only for freaks, eccentrics or people who would never get married otherwise. But surely if we were really honest with ourselves, we should choose our partners scientifically. Take myself. How am I likely to meet the ideal barmaid? Yet, if only marriage bureaux were patronized by ordinary, decent people, not simply by desperately frustrated and lonely souls, I could obtain a dossier on various barmaids who had the qualities I mentioned and the interests I possess. They, similarly, could have a list of my likes, dislikes and eccentricities.'

'You mean, if we were really civilized, we should all use marriage bureaux as a matter of course?'

'Exactly. Not in any suspicious, cold-blooded manner, but as a sensible precaution. It would prevent a lot of unhappiness and save many divorces. The Church might well give a lead in this direction.'

Well, Martyn Bowker is still considering this idea, but, as he says, in a village one must move with discretion and with a weather eye on the emotional climate of the Mothers' Union. A bachelor dabbling in a Lonely Hearts' Club would be just the topic for ribald and Rabelaisian comment at the Bearpits. All the same he has made one cautious step: the barbecue party for unattached teenagers at the vicarage garden was a great success, even though it was made plain that 'squares' were welcomed, a piece of subtlety that discouraged the wilder of the Henty rock 'n' rollers.

East Sussex has been the home of many distinguished, individualistic and remarkable divines. The Reverend E. F. Synnott, an incumbent of Iden, was not only an amateur boxing champion in his youth, but wrote a book entitled *Five Years Hell in a County Parish* about another Sussex village – Rusper. The Vicar of Northiam is a member of the Magic Circle, his own species of magic being the art of escaping from sealed cupboards. At Ticehurst, as the 'Live Letter Box' of the *Daily Mirror* recently testified through various correspondents, the former vicar, the Reverend Arthur Eden, maintained a full-operational beer-engine in his vicarage: 'I remember the Rev. Arthur Eden when I was a maid in a doctor's house in Ticehurst,' stated one writer. 'Whenever the vicar paid us an afternoon call it was always tea in the drawing-room for the ladies – but beer for Mr. Eden. He was a grand old man!'

I make these points because far too often an unreal, unsympathetic and dreary picture is painted of country clergymen. Not only is this uncharitable, but, even to my non-sectarian eye, it just isn't true. Martyn Bowker is a realist: his sermons are brief, unpretentious, but effective. If there is one type of sermon your man of Sussex detests it is a diffuse, circumlocutionary tangle of theology and textual analysis. 'That canon we had larst Sunday bain't a patch on our vicar,' said Mrs. Notley, our twice-weekly help. 'He did beat the devil round the gooseberry bush so.'[1]

---

[1] Take a long time to get to the point.

Our vicar may not have such talents as the Vicar of Northiam, nor may be so outspoken as the boxing, author-rector of Iden. But, if he hasn't a beer-engine operating in his vicarage, he enjoys a glass of beer, or sherry, and sometimes ventures into the Hole in the Wall. He is certainly not unmindful of the thirst of the people around him. If you go into the main porch of the Church of Saint Mildred, you will see what I mean.

There, quite conspicuously placed, is an old brown pitcher, with a lace cloth over it. Beside the pitcher is a notice in Gothic lettering: 'Fresh spring water for weary travellers.' There is a jug, with three glasses alongside.

Once or twice a year some vandal breaks a glass, or out of some senseless hatred steals one. But replacements are always made – paid for by the vicar, whose idea it was, and which is a great boon to visitors on a hot Sunday afternoon.

J. MARCABANK SALMON

12. *Treasure hunt with the Women's Institute*

IT wasn't until late spring that we awoke to the fact that there was a fairyland at the bottom of our garden.

For months we had regarded the hollow, now mercifully cleared of all rubble, weed and decaying vegetation, as a quarter of an acre of futility translated into matter. Then, one intoxicatingly radiant afternoon in late April, having lost sight of my wife, I was informed by my son that she had 'gone down to the hollow half an hour ago'.

Heavens, I thought, this could be serious! Sylvia had always abominated the hollow. For her to go down there and stay for half an hour suggested all manner of dreadful things. Had she fallen down a hidden well? Had she been bitten by a snake? Hastily withdrawing myself from the depths of a deck-chair, I ran to the top of the hollow and, looking down into it, was horrified to see Sylvia, her eyes closed, lying flat on her back.

But I need not have worried. She was complacently all right. Her nonchalant explanation was that she had suddenly realized that what the Oast House lacked was a snug, south-western aspect in the garden. Taking out her key-ring, which was fitted with a miniature compass, she found that, if she walked in a south-westerly direction, she came to the hollow. She climbed down to the bottom and revelled in the shelter provided and the ogling warmth of the afternoon sun. Smug in her sybaritic, helophilous syllogism, she curled up cosily and murmured:

'Obviously, darling, we have failed to appreciate that the hollow is really our greatest asset. You must bring the summer-house down here. It really is a sun-trap. And just look at that glorious view.'

I looked and she was indisputably right. It was not only a view, but an unspoiled example of hylotheism. Beyond the barbed wire fence at the foot of the hollow was a meadow ablaze with poppies. At the end of the meadow was a copse of trees bordering Bearpits Lane, on the other side of which lay the geometrically perfect hop-gardens, with their clusters of oasts. Then, on slightly higher ground, sheltering the hop-gardens, were woods nestling against the lower slopes of distant downs, oaks and beeches fading out into pines and firs. It was an absolutely superb cross-section of the Sussex countryside. And on that soft, spring-kissed afternoon, with April painting in poppies on a green background and the sunshine bathing the oasts in red gold, one could almost agree with Shelley's sublime optimist that . . .

> Life, like a dome of many-coloured glass,
> Stains the white radiance of eternity.

After that 'the hollow' became a quarter acre of land consecrated to Calliope. If no epic poems were written about it, our thoughts were on an epic plane and the converted oast-cowl summer-house was transported to the bottom of the hollow and placed so that it faced south-west. Slowly, but inexorably, we created a rock garden where there had been a wilderness. The barbed-wire fence was pulled up and replaced by a small brick wall, built by Jim Bricknell out of the hundreds of bricks which had been dug up around the Oast House. There were enough bricks left over to make steps down from the garden into the hollow.

A rock garden is one of those projects which look easy, but are full of unforseen snags. First of all, the rocks: if you choose the wrong type of stone, you will find them all split by frosts when winter gets under way. Secondly, unless you choose your plants carefully, you will eventually find not a rock garden, but a prolific luxuriance of weeds. And weeding among rocks is no joke. Long before the summer was over we discovered a particularly vicious-looking weed among the stones. Some might have called it semi-tropical, but it conjured up, not visions of bougainvillaea or hibiscus, but of a derelict plantation. The wretched weed wasn't even modest; it grew to a height of four feet with branches spreading out to three feet, produced a trumpet-shaped, whitish flower which later gave place to a round spiky capsule, not unlike a horse-chestnut, full of seeds. Eva pronounced it to be a Cuckold's Apple, which, she said, only appeared once in twenty years in these parts. Sir Oswald Thyme's gardener, with more detachment, assured me it was a *Datura Stramonium* and 'exceedingly poisonous'. Personally we settled for 'Strontium 90' and this is the name it has had *chez nous* ever since.

To prevent the invasion of weeds we filled the rock garden with aubrietia and rock rose, and as a rider to this brief incursion into a subject about which I know very little, I would add that aubrietia is to the lazy gardener absolute manna. It just spreads and spreads, eating up all the space which weeds normally occupy and, for the trouble it saves, I would rather have it than rose trees any day.

Rhododendrons, which wouldn't grow anywhere else around the Oast, flourished in the peaty loam of the hollow. Experts will tell you that rhododendrons are difficult to grow unless the soil is specially prepared. Frankly, I doubt whether you can ever do much with them, however much trouble you take, unless you have a peaty loam. Then they are no trouble at all.

Eva had a summer routine of her own. She gardened until lunch-time, then went round to the Bearpits and disappeared until about 6 p.m. She would then set to work again until about an hour before closing time at the Hole in the Wall. She called her evening session of work her 'tighting up'. I was rather apprehensive when first she used this expression as, when asked how she was after visiting the Bearpits on the morning after, she would always reply: 'I'm pretty tightish, thank you.' But we learned that 'tightish' in this context meant 'in good health' and 'tighting up' was cleaning, or putting in order.

'Tighting up' often went on until long after dark. It was a phrase which covered anything from mending a deck-chair, repairing the hose, recovering golf balls from the flower-beds to hunting for wireworms, click beetles, blight, or raspberry weevils. Two things Eva was absolutely fanatical about were manure and raspberry weevils. For a long time I couldn't make out what on earth she meant when she talked of 'moving the amendment tonight'; I supposed she was making some formal proposal to the committee of the Bearpits' Darts Club. Eventually I arrived at the conclusion that the 'amendment' was the manure. As to raspberry weevils, from the end of July to the end of August they positively obsessed her. When she wasn't talking about 'moving amendments', or buying some dried blood, she was chasing the weevils. She had discovered a few rows of raspberry canes left over from heaven knows how long ago and had fussed and footled around them all summer. For the sake of her precious raspberry canes, over which she hovered like a hen over her chicks, Eva would stay in the garden until after dusk waiting for the weevils to appear. 'I'll get 'em,' she would mutter darkly. 'I'll get 'em, if it's the last thing I do.' And she disappeared into the gloom, her bulky shape merging into what looked from a distance like a scarecrow with waving arms. Out of the darkness at regular intervals came ripe Sussex oaths as Eva grappled with the revolting, quarter-inch long weevils and their messy, yellow, hairless grubs. She would shake the canes, hoping to collect the weevils as they fell, but I am sure they raced up the stems again as soon as she bent down to gather them. Somehow both Eva and the raspberries survived.

A more successful nocturnal excursion of Eva's was her battle with the greenfly. After raspberries Eva's next favourite fruit was plums and to her horror she found our Pershore Yellow Egg and the more stately Reine Claude de Bavay were being insidiously attacked by greenfly. 'You go to bed too early,' she grunted. 'Doan't yer know a gardener should never go abed early this time of the year. You stay up tonight until it's time for the farisees to come out. I'll look round after they pack up at the Hole – we've a darts match there at nine o'clock – and see you 'ave the insecticide gun filled. Then we'll 'ave some rare old fun under the trees.'

One didn't argue with Eva. She would, as they say in Sussex, 'never be druv,' and there was nothing but to wait up for her. So on several nights I lingered with her under the plum trees while she sprayed and cursed and cursed and sprayed and adjured me to 'give 'em a spray with tar oil wash next winter.' On really hot nights this operation was usually interrupted by the appearance of Sylvia with a bottle of perry and three glasses.

'Tell me, Eva,' I said, as I filled her glass, 'what are these farisees you speak of? When do we see them?'

'Farisees is the little fellows wot makes the fairy-rings, them circles you see on the grass. That's the farisees dancing that does that.'

'You mean fairies? Have you ever seen any?'

'Surelye, but not since the war I ain't. There used to be farisees down in Ghost Wood. Little chaps not quite as big as a fox, but bigger'n a squirrel. Course these atom bombs and such like 'ave chased 'em all away. But happen you go to Romney Marsh, you'll see 'em there.'

Eva was always willing to talk about farisees. She told Anthony that he must rub some cuckoo spit on his right hand and then, if he went down to the hollow after dusk, he might see the farisees dancing in a ring. And Eva became very angry indeed if anyone doubted her word.

These midnight perry-drinking sessions developed into what Sylvia and I called our language classes. In the span of three or four glasses of perry we learned a wealth of Sussex dialect. The extraordinary thing was that on many occasions Eva, like others in the remoter parts of the county, spoke pure Shakespeare. It was absolutely uncanny. I made a list of her choicest phrases and, sure enough, a little diligent research soon proved that most of them could be found in the works of the Bard. The clown in *All's Well That Ends Well* talks of the 'sweet marjoram of the sallet'; Eva, too, used this word for salad and, when she spoke of 'mommicking' a job, she borrowed directly from *Coriolanus*.

One could go on with this game indefinitely. To Eva most men were 'runagates' – unreliable, lecherous and rascally – just as Shakespeare ranted . . .

> 'There let him sink, and be the seas on him!
> White-livered runagate, what doth he there?'

Odds and ends were 'orts', those 'fractions of her faith, orts of her love,' of which the Bard wrote in *Troilus and Cressida*. A pregnant girl was 'quick' just like the poor wench in *Love's Labour Lost*. When I asked Eva the name of the flowers of *orchis mascula*, she replied: 'Wot, them long purples? In Codgem we calls 'em torn maidenheads.' And I thought of the Queen of Denmark, finding Ophelia in her watery grave under the willows, bedecked with 'fantastic garlands', and saying. . .

> '. . . and long purples,
> That liberal shepherds give a grosser name.'

But there was much else that neither Shakespeare, nor Fletcher, who was born at Rye, had borrowed from the Sussex tongue. Much else we learned from Eva and Young George at the Merry Damsel; phrases which gave their sentences a rhythmic ring, a dancing rhythm such as one finds in the dialogue of Congreve, not perhaps the polished sophistication of Congreve, but the same sharp uptake at the end of a sentence, a chiming and a tinkling of words, a spontaneity that was never marred by the rural habit of reiteration. 'If you says a word to 'im, 'ee's top of the house drackly minnut,' was a favourite expression of Young George.

K

'Top of the house' meant a person who had lost his temper and 'drackly minnut' was immediately. I liked Eva's description of Miss Ablethorpe taking her constitutional round Cucking Green: 'she doddles to-and-agin' and her delightfully picturesque phrase for those limpid June nights – 'print-moonlight'.

This badinage on greenfly and weevils, plums and perry, enlivened by Eva's lusty, flamboyant, sometimes Elizabethan, occasionally tippety-tap Restoration dialogue, was mainly conducted in the hours of print-moonlight. Even if the farisees never showed themselves, there was a Puckish, sprite-evoking atmosphere under the trees so that it seemed at any moment Peas-Blossom, Cobweb, Moth and Mustard-Seed must start mafficking on the lawn.

.   .   .   .   .

The days and nights of that splendid summer merged gaily into one magic-carpet transported adventure. There were the songs of the birds to tape-record, while lying lazily on a rug under the firs; our first barbecue party at which 'Bifty' Etheridge acted as chef and for which Bronwen provided the perry; that cherished extra half-hour in fading light on Cucking Green when Codiham were fighting for runs on a slippery wicket; the monthly meetings at the Hole in the Wall to plan Codiham United's tactics for next season. There were inquisitive excursions into the unknown countryside, happy-go-lucky meanderings across Weald and distant downs, simply to find some place the maps did not show.

It is surprising what maps will miss and we soon discovered that the Ordnance Survey omitted many fascinating places. Now and again in some second-hand shop at Tunbridge Wells or Hastings we would come across an ancient map full of surprising data that modern cartographers had discarded as unimportant. This started us off on a new game – trying to locate the tumuli, Roman earthworks and other historical sites described on the old maps. On one such sixteenth-century map of Codiham I found a triangle designated 'The Fisheries'; this, I felt sure, must refer to the Parson's Catch. There was also a tumulus marked as 'Fort Tolls'. The position of this intrigued me; it lay on the fringe of the Downs due south-west of Codiham, though no modern map gave any indication of it.

Anthony was the first to spot it. Using the chart and a compass, he scanned the horizon with the binoculars from the summer-house in the hollow. There, like a pin-point on a ridge of the Downs, was a very definite tumulus, not more than thirty feet in height, with two or three trees growing on the summit. Nobody knew much about the tumulus locally; the villagers referred to it vaguely as Roman's Hump, which certainly suggested earthworks of some kind, though local history books made no mention of Roman remains in the vicinity. The tumulus must have been removed from local maps three hundred years ago and 'Fort Tolls' rang no bell of recollection in the ear of even the most erudite and ancient inhabitant. Indeed, as far as we could make out, nobody in the whole village had ever visited the place. Some denied its existence and suggested the tumulus was a mirage – 'one of they mizmazed images you gets on the Marsh in September.'

To a boy for whom ancient maps are as romantic as pieces of eight, doubloons and moidores, the tumulus, 'Fort Tolls', Roman's Hump, or what-you-will, was a challenge. Anthony insisted on setting out alone to find it. Armed with the binoculars, some garden tools he had borrowed from Eva, and a package of sandwiches, he climbed the wall at the bottom of the hollow and set out in quest of the tumulus with all the enthusiasm of an explorer going into uncharted territory. Across the meadows, through a hole in a hedge and on into the woods he went, more than once losing sight of his objective, but using his compass to guide him. There wasn't a farm or a cottage within two miles of the tumulus, but when he reached the foot of the Downs there was no mistaking that neither the ancient map, nor the binoculars had lied. There were the distinct remains of a vallum, possibly the site of a fortified Roman settlement long before Codiham was founded. Probably at one time the sea came right up to this ancient earthworks and the Romans landed nearby. Anthony made a rough map of the immediate area, proudly returning home, not with the Roman coins, or tiles, which he had hoped to find, but at least with something that our village historian and curator of the tiny museum proclaimed was 'remarkably like a Roman nail'.

I have since talked with farmers in many parts of East Sussex, but found them almost unanimously reticent on the subject of Roman remains. I suspect there may be many similar unnoted earthworks in this part of the county, but, as one of the farmers bluntly put it: 'Wot with they inspectors and blurry bureaucrats, we've 'ad enough people traipsing over our fields and we don't want no Archies digging us up for summat you can't eat anyhow.'

The gradual encroachment of bureaucracy into agriculture has hardened the hearts of many farmers, who, it must be admitted, are congenitally inclined to regard the world outside their fields as hostile. It may well be that planning and inspection have, by and large, helped farming, that they have weeded out many incompetents and instilled some modern notions into stubborn minds. But surely the vital lesson of such experiments is that, if pushed too far, they fail to allow for the intransigent human element and therefore fail. Farmers, whether the isolationists of the Middle West, the gold-hoarding reactionaries of the Auvergne, or the hard-bargaining money-grubbers of the Sussex Weald, are an anarchistic community the whole world over; they keep their sights low and close to the ground, regard charity as a dirty word and laugh only in the tap-room. Stalin thought he could conquer them and consequently gravely overestimated what planning could achieve. Mao Tse-Tung, more wisely, refused to follow the communist line on agriculture with the result that today Stalin is decried and Mao Tse-Tung is back in the orthodox Marxist fold, his prestige immensely greater. Yet even today throughout the communist world the farmer is largely unconquered. I quote from a report from Eastern Europe: 'Agricultural performance in Yugoslavia had been poor up to 1951, and in 1952 the regime found it expedient to abandon compulsory deliveries. In response to peasant resistance the Government permitted members of collectives to withdraw their land after the 1953 harvest.'

I have found farmers who reluctantly admit that planning may have helped them to market their goods more effectively. 'I doan't say as 'ow those agricultural advisory chaps aren't useful fellows in useful jobs. Wot I do say is that if some poor devil who ain't got much cash makes a hash of things, the planners push un out. But they doan't push out them amateur farmers, those stockbroker fellows like that Sosserthwaite who only farms to dodge their taxes.'

Farmers, too, feel that all Governments tend to squeeze them out – 'to hedge us in in smaller circles all the time.' They view with gloom the projects to grab agricultural land for industrial development and nuclear power stations. In so tiny and overpopulated an island as Britain the traditional conservatism and stubbornness of the farmer is not likely to be eradicated by such psychological blunders by bureaucrats.

'First it was they jets,' one told me. 'They came whining over our lands night and day. When they closed the fighter bases, we thought perhaps we ud 'ave some peace. But, bless yer life, no. Now they want to put up this blessed nuclear power station at Dungeness. "Is it safe?" I asks 'em. "Oh, yes, it's safe enough," they says. "Well, if it's safe, why not put un up in an industrial area where it wouldn't interfere with farming?"

I asks. "Oah, no," they replies, "we couldn't do that, cos if it wasn't safe, then we'd 'ave to move it."

' "But you says it is safe," I says. "So tis," they says, "but we got to be careful like." If you asks me, they doan't know wot's safe and wot isn't. Not yet anyhow. And we farmers are the blurry guinea-pigs. Look at all that Zeeta talk. The nuclear power firms' shares zoomed like jets when they first mentioned Zeeta. Now they've all dropped agin. You can't tell me they've dropped for no reason.'

Yet all over Sussex, with the exception of certain scheduled areas of park and downland, the Central Electricity Generating Board have taken over many acres of farmland on the plea of producing cheaper electricity for the homes and industry of the south.

·   ·   ·   ·   ·

One of the most amusing events of that summer was the Women's Institute Treasure Hunt.

I had always thought that the Women's Institute was a cross between the Mother's Union, the Band of Hope and a grandmother's sewing circle. Or at the best a female version of the Working Men's Club. It was, therefore, with something of a shock that I received the news from Sylvia that she had thought of going along to one of their meetings.

'Better remove all your make-up,' I suggested. 'And put on a pair of red flannel knickers, too. You must play the part.'

For which remarks I had a cushion hurled at me.

I was swiftly brought to realize that the W.I. is an exceedingly joyful organization and one that, despite its fondness for singing *Jerusalem* as a theme song, knows when to let its hair down and make the welkin ring. Perhaps I am wrong even to refer to it in the neuter gender. In fact I will now go on record as saying that any study of modern village life which ignores the Women's Institute is probably worthless. The W.I., certainly in Sussex, is as much a rallying point of village life as the Church or the pub.

Any historian of social life in Britain today should read *Your Village*, edited by Inez Jenkins and published by the National Federation of Women's Institutes. It is an admirable reference book on rural sociology, serious, factual, well documented and based on the research of thousands of W.I. members throughout Britain.

A questionnaire was sent out to 7,000 Women's Institutes, most of which sent in the answers required. *Your Village* reveals only too clearly that, despite the vast improvement in services in the towns, many villages lag far behind in such matters as schools, water supplies, sanitation and fuel. Calor gas and septic tanks still dominate many areas. Several Sussex villages depend on shallow surface wells for their drinking water; in the whole country 1,468 villages have inadequate water supplies, 998 have no electricity at all, while, even more surprising, 4,124 have nothing they can call a recreation ground.

In such areas the W.I. is of the utmost importance. Despite the arrival of television, it survives as the focal point of social life for countless women and has the attraction of being as near to a classless entity as any you will find in the whole land. Francis Brett Young wrote of Women's Institute meetings that, 'in the case of Monk's Norton – though the ladies who started them would honestly and indignantly deny it – was a subtle and indirect form of political propaganda unnecessary before the working man's wife got a vote: an attempt to prove that the colonel's lady and Judy O'Grady were sisters, that the gulf which unhappily separated their standards of living was quite unimportant compared with their fundamental community of sex.'

In the 'thirties, when these words were written, this may have been true of the Women's Institute in some areas, but I doubt whether it applies anywhere today. Certainly in Codiham there is no evidence of such subtlety. Doubtless twenty years ago Miss Ablethorpe would have been W.I. chairman; today she would be as out of place in that organization as a Quaker at a mass, though occasionally welcomed as a guest speaker. As for Codiham's 'colonel's lady', in the person of Mrs. Skinner, I am sure that after a quarter of a century spent in India and a total inability to understand post-war Britain, she would have been singularly ineffective. The gulf which separates her living standards from those of the average villager is that she has no television set, no washing machine, electric mixer or spin-drier, while her daily help has.

The Women's Institute in Codiham has changed like most other institutions. The sewing bees of the 'thirties, the jumble sales and sing-songs, the talks on jam-making and rose-pruning, the whist drives and socials have given place to a weekly market of fruit and vegetables grown by members, to lectures on psychology by Dr. Gillebrand and Bronwen Pritchard's art classes, to an annual drama festival at Cucking Manor, a W.I. darts team, baby-sitting rosters and L.P. recitals.

Lady Thyme is the driving force behind the local W.I. She is young enough to attract the younger women of the village and influential enough to hold the goodwill of the few remaining pre-war members. It was she who persuaded her husband to let the W.I. meet in the ballroom at Cucking Manor: 'the village hall is much too drab,' she argued. 'Why should any woman with a home of her own want to exchange it for the discomfort of hard wooden benches and a stinking coke stove?'

I think that the atmosphere of the Manor ballroom did something to the W.I. members. If at first they were somewhat awed by going to the Manor, they soon warmed to its faded opulence, its tapestries and frescoes. For the village women it was much more of a night out than a visit to the village hall. 'Doc' Gillebrand is a stalwart supporter of the W.I.; one might almost say he is the best recruiting officer they have. With his zest for practical cures for ill health and nervous diseases, he often prescribes membership of the W.I. as 'a real chance to make friends and escape from household drudgery.' When husbands protest to him that he is seducing their wives from the firesides and encouraging 'too much independence', he retorts that they are far more likely to have efficient housewives, cooks and organizers, if their spouses join the Institute.

Which to a very large extent is true. The W.I. puts into women's minds many useful ideas which they swiftly translate into action in their homes. It stimulates a spirit of friendly competition and rivalry, not only among members in Codiham, but against the neighbouring Institutes and there is always the urge to put on a good show at the Lewes Exhibition. Codiham W.I. boasts of having the best drama team in East Sussex and their darts side, though never challenging the men, often makes coach trips to other villages.

I said that Miss Ablethorpe would be out of her element in the modern W.I. As a member this is undoubtedly true, but after the Cucking Green controversy and the publicity about the mysterious goings-on around the Pond, the natural curiosity of W.I. members prompted an invitation to her to address them. The subject was – well, yes, you have guessed correctly – 'Beatniks, Teddy Boys and Modern Youth.'

Codiham is not unique in its choice of W.I. activities. I have before me a copy of the *Sussex County Herald* and I quote from its weekly column on Women's Institutes, for, although these comments do not concern Codiham, they are about neighbouring W.I.s and indicate clearly how varied are their recreations:

'Etchingham W.I. . . . the competition – a table decoration made of leaves – was won by Mrs. E. Wells.

Northiam W.I. . . . Highlight of the evening was to hear that Mrs. Banister had won the women's competition for a play.

Playden W.I. . . . [the] meeting heard plans for the forthcoming barbecue and Guy Fawkes supper.

Peasmarsh W.I. . . . An interesting talk was given by Mrs. Webb about "Elephants on my Doorstep".

Westfield W.I. . . . An amusing talk on "The History of Underclothes" was given by Mrs. Marsden-Smedley.'

The highlight of W.I. activities in Codiham that summer was the Treasure Hunt. I forget just what deserving cause was to benefit through this event, but the idea was that anyone wishing to participate must pay half-a-crown for a sealed envelope containing the typewritten instructions for the Hunt.

There had been so much secrecy about this Treasure Hunt while it was being planned that the husbands of the village had begun to get restive. Usually husbands chose to pretend to ignore W.I. activities. I suspect that most of them were rather jealous of the fun which their wives derived from it. But they could hardly ignore the fact that there was to be a Treasure Hunt. At breakfast time they would be told: 'I shan't be in this evening. There's a Treasure Hunt meeting.' Or, when they came home, it would be: 'Perhaps you would like to get your own supper tonight, as I may not be back till late. The Treasure Hunt, you know.' And for weeks they were constantly reminded to keep a certain Saturday free because 'It's the Treasure Hunt and you've got to come.'

'This flippin' Treasure Hunt,' grumbled Jonathan Henty, 'it's properly disorganizing life. Wot's more I suspect it's a blatant bit of capitalist propaganda.'

'Sailor' Thompsett rudely suggested that 'this Treaure Hunt was a stunt for the gels only' and that François L'Amour was to be the 'treasure'. 'You watch out, Frenchy,' he told the barman-goalkeeper, 'whoever finds you on the day ull take you 'ome for keeps.' He so scared François that the barman asked for leave to go to Boulogne on the date on which the Hunt was to be held.

But 'Sailor' was wrong. It turned out that the Treasure Hunt was for 'men only'. 'Bifty' Etheridge, ever zealous in his untiring quest for women, decided that 'Sailor' might have got very near the truth. 'Could be,' he said, 'that the gels have decided to give us a treat and that the Treasure is one of Codgem's cutest "cuckers".' He even managed to spy through the ballroom of Cucking Manor and listen in to the discussions of a Treasure Hunt Committee meeting.

'I couldn't hear very much, but I have a hunch there may be some fun in this, old boy,' he whispered to me. 'Bronwen is in on it and I overheard Ulrica Thyme say she has asked down a party of friends from London. Just to hot things up. Also, and this is very significant, Ulrica Thyme and Flossie Whitcombe were in deep confab. I think Flossie is to fix up a beer tent.'

That was only part of the story. What 'Bifty' omitted to tell was that he was caught snooping by Lady Thyme and warned that if he didn't make himself scarce, he would be banned from taking any part in the hunt. Ulrica was, according to 'Bifty', 'a honey, a dish, a darling,' but the honey turned to cold, congealed dripping when she gave him a dressing-down.

The hunt was held in the gardens of Cucking Manor. There were the usual side-shows – skittles, darts, bowling for a pig, fruit and vegetables, home-made cakes and jam stalls. And, sure enough, Flossie Whitcombe was presiding at a beer tent and Young George, loaned for the occasion by Mr. Pargetter, and clad in a white coat, was serving wines and spirits in a red-and-white marquee.

'Bifty' and I, having bought our sealed envelopes enclosing the instructions for the Treasure Hunt, went along to refresh ourselves in the beer tent before we started.

'Collect a Grandmother's Nightcap, the fruit of a Merry Tree and bring them to the bench under the stables clock where you will be given another ticket in exchange,' stated my instruction card.

'Good God!' said 'Bifty', 'this looks like an exercise in Sussex dialect. I know a Merry Tree is a cherry tree, but damned if I know whether they really want some grandma's nightcap, or if it's the name of some flower.'

We wandered off round the gardens, found a couple of cherries easily enough and met Colonel Skinner who had apparently been given a different set of instructions.

'Dam' thirsty work this, I must say,' he roared. 'Does anyone know what the hell a greybeard is?'

'Why,' replied 'Bifty', 'it's an earthen jug used for beer. You might be able to borrow one at the Bearpits.'

'Ah, well, I suppose if one goes in for this sort of nonsense, one may as well make the best of it,' said the Colonel. 'I'll pop up to the Bearpits and see. But I hope this isn't some dam' fool trick of yours.'

But even 'Bifty' didn't know what a Grandmother's Nightcap was. I'm afraid I stole an unfair march on him there. I slipped off to buy Sir Oswald Thyme's head gardener a drink and learned it was the Sussex name for white campion.

It soon became obvious why the Treasure Hunt was for men only. This was not only a ruse to make the men delve into their pockets for half crowns, but a subtle plot by their womenfolk to obtain secret enjoyment of their discomfiture. It reduced us all to rather pathetic figures of fun as, clutching such objects as cherries, white campion, bird's nests, honey-pots, mouse-traps, corsets and, when Colonel Skinner returned from the Bearpits, a beer jug, we trooped over to the bench under the stables clock, delivered our 'clues' and collected other tickets.

By early evening the more despondent and less adaptable husbands had shamefacedly given up the chase. They preferred to retire to the Merry Damsel than to retain what few shreds of prestige remained. Meanwhile my second ticket instructed me to proceed to the Palladian Bridge and hang a Chinese lantern on one of the arches. After this I would be given another ticket . . . .

A party of Lady Thyme's London friends had received a similar set of instructions. They poured themselves into a small coupé and sped off in the direction of Tunbridge Wells where one of them claimed to know a 'Chinese restaurant that might help'. I felt that this was where my rapidly acquired Codgem lore would give me an advantage; if anybody could produce a Chinese lantern quickly, it would be old Harry Sprogget. After all he stocked tinned Chinese food in the recesses of his Ali Baba's cave of a general stores.

Harry, I might add, is as cunning as they come. For when I called in Sprogget & Sons, he grinned broadly, led me into his store-room below stairs and pointed to about a dozen Chinese lanterns.

'Harry, you old devil,' I said, 'I believe you knew this was to be one of the clues. You had a spy in the W.I. camp.'

' "Us be proper wicked down at Codgem",' he mumbled. 'If I don't sell 'em all today, happen as people ul want 'em at Christmas.'

It was Bronwen Pritchard who greeted me on the Palladian Bridge, when I returned to hang up my dragon-emblazoned lantern. 'You are only the second person to put one up,' she said. 'How very useful the men are being this afternoon. All our bridge decorations done for nothing. Are you enjoying yourself?'

'Like hell I am,' I replied. 'Whose crazy idea was this? It sounds like an occupational therapy exercise set by "Doc" Gillebrand.'

'I assure you it isn't. We planned this most carefully all last winter. The real fun is yet to come. We anticipated that you men would find the going hard, so Lady Thyme arranged for a party of some of her Town friends to provide some competition. And also some transport. Some clues are only obtainable at an hour's travelling at Jaguar speed. Here's your next ticket.'

The real fun was certainly yet to come! My next instructions sent me in quest of 'a stone nymph with green eyes'. Dragging my weary body through the rhododendron bushes, tripping over low-lying branches, I wandered among the statues of fauns and satyrs created by the rake-hell, Sir Walter. I had just pitched on my face, when I was greeted by Mrs. Jephson, a W.I. member whom I had always suspected of being a practical joker.

'Have you lost something?' she asked.

'I'm looking for a nymph with green eyes,' was my lame response.

'Surely she's not in the bushes. Perhaps she's gone to have a drink.'

'Come to that,' I said, 'what are you doing here?'

'Oh, I'm just enjoying the fun. I've already seen Colonel Skinner crawling on his knees in search of Venus's looking glass. I must say you men have lived up to your reputations for having one-track minds today.'

If the ghost of Sir Walter had appeared that night he might have believed that this was the beginning of a rake-hell party. The garden plot laid out in the likeness of a nude woman pursued by Bacchus was full of husbands searching for green-eyed nymphs, the oval pool that was Venus' looking glass and variously oddly named satyrs. This part of the Hunt had been cunningly devised so that it took us a long way from the beer tent.

Colonel Skinner eventually found his next clue in the shape of a paper-boat floating on the oval pool. My green-eyed nymph bore a card which told me to go to the barbecue, grill three sausages and exchange them for another ticket. And, of course, the sausages weren't provided. I had to go to Sprogget's to buy them, noting that that cunning old rascal was keeping open long after his normal closing hour.

I very nearly ate the sausages when I had grilled them; I was quite famished after so much exhausting chasing hither and thither. However, I'm glad I didn't give up the quest then for, as Bronwen Pritchard had said, the real fun was yet to come. This consisted, so my next ticket told me, of a quick tour of the village – to drink an October Ale at the Damsel, to eat a pork-pie at the Bearpits and consume a pint of draught cider at the Hole, for each of which items a receipt had to be obtained.

This enabled the twelve remaining men in the Hunt to swop experiences in Codiham's three pubs, to escape, temporarily at least, from the sadistically gleeful watchfulness of our womenfolk. I'm afraid I didn't win the Treasure Hunt, but that didn't matter. I shared in the prize just the same. It was a barrel of cider and won by 'Ginger' Pearson.

.   .   .   .   .

Mrs. Notley, our domestic help, worked in the hop-gardens in the summer. She had done this for more than twenty years and, in consequence, was our chief source of information on hops and hopping. A sprightly, fiftyish, hair-in-a-bun, reed-like woman, she never seemed to eat anything but 'scraps' and drink innumerable cups of tea. 'Scraps' was her designation of any meal she took and, though an excellent cook, who believed that men needed 'feeding up like Turkey cocks,' she rarely ate more than a few biscuits, milk pudding and salad stuff. If you asked her what she would have, she would invariably say, 'Oh, just a scrap of summat.' This lack of food didn't in any way affect her health, or her disposition. She was as lean as a beanstalk, but, as she put it, 'I can get about faster that way.'

Mrs. Notley and Eva didn't approve of one another. Mrs. Notley considered herself a cut above Eva and sniffed condescendingly about 'women wot does gardening', with a few veiled hints that seemed to suggest she cast doubts on Eva's heterosexuality. Eva, for her part, called Mrs. Notley 'Skinny Sal' and argued that she would be much better if she drank Guinness.

Nicholas Culpeper in his *English Physitian, enlarged,* of 1695, claimed that the hop is one of the most useful adjuncts of the medicine cupboard. According to him, it has blood-cleansing properties and medicinally both the young shoots and the flowers are valuable. He stated that syrups of hop-flowers are a cure for fevers and scurvy. Mrs. Notley, who has never heard of Culpeper, insists that a pillow filled with hops is the only sure cure for insomnia and that the young shoots, when three inches from the ground, are delicious if boiled and eaten – 'the poor man's asparagus' she calls them.

Generally speaking, there would seem to be as many different types of hop as there are varieties of beer. Constant cultivation, coupled with agonizing reappraisals in the light of brewers' criticisms, and realization that particular soils suit different hops, have led to the evolution of specimens which are spoken of with a reverence that is more usually associated with the grape. The type grown mostly around Codiham is the Golding, which is large, perfect in shape and among the richest and choicest of all hops. An unusual hop, not much in favour with most growers because it does not produce a heavy crop, is Bates's Brewers. One hop farmer in the village swears by Bates's Brewers and claims it produces the best beer of all. It is said that the six sets yielded by the original plant, grown by a Mr. John Bates, of Brenchley in Kent in 1880, were sold for a bottle of whisky apiece.

Not so many of the East Enders of London come down to the Weald hop-picking these days. Holidays with pay, full employment and the introduction of hop-picking machines have made these excursions less profitable. But the truth is that a hop-picking machine does not replace the skilled picker entirely and brewers say that machine-picked hops are not up to the standard of hand-picked. The machine takes about twenty-five people to operate it, compared to the same output from about a hundred hand-pickers.

Even today about fifty men, women and children come down from London to join the local hop-pickers and bring with them all the appendages of modern civilization – trailer caravans, television sets, long-players. They seem strangely out of place alongside the local hop-pickers, who rather resent their arrogance and display of material wealth and note sourly that the Londoners always have enough cash to buy double-Scotches at the Bearpits. But the annual Hoppers' Ball on Cucking Green is a mellowing influence and breaks down a good deal of mutual hostility. It is enlivened by the presence of Romany folk who always put in an appearance at hopping-time, making it a point of honour to call at Bronwen Pritchard's home. The Romanies have a remarkable bush-telegraph system – how much of it is telepathic, or based on secret signs scrawled on people's doors, I don't know – but they inevitably track down those who are their friends and sympathizers.

The Hoppers' Ball consists of uninhibited, if not particularly skilful dancing on the Green, accompanied by the raucous singing of such familiar ditties as ' Knock 'em in the Old Kent Road,' 'Knees up, Mother Brown' and 'Gertcher, do you take me for a Silly'. Round the Green is all the fun of the fair to provide an appropriate background for all this frollicking: coconut shies, a merry-go-round, clay-pigeon shooting and such hoary side-shows as the inevitable blousy, hair-dyed damsel to be knocked out of bed in a wire cage, a fortune-telling caravan where gypsies demand the traditional silver to cross their palms, and the Codiham Brass Band with its sonorous, laboured efforts to introduce a boomps-a-daisy note into the proceedings. It is quite a good brass band as such bands go, but a little too serious-minded for a fair. The bandmaster has an unfortunate prediliction for playing 'Sussex by the Sea', which he is apt to repeat at too frequent intervals. This may be an admirable theme-song for Codiham United F.C., but not for Cockneys in holiday mood, ardently bent on fox-trotting round the Green to a lively, jazzy number.

As the fifty East Enders induce all their relatives and friends to descend on the village on the night of the Hoppers' Ball, Codiham loses no opportunity of making money while it has the chance. Not only do the pubs keep open half an hour later, thanks to the lenience of the Licensing Justices, but local shop-keepers are not above altering their price tags for the occasion. If they do, the East Enders have only themselves to blame by flaunting their new-found and infrequently declared wealth.

This is also an occasion for the farmers of the district to meet in the Bearpits and discuss plans for the autumn Fat Stock Show, sounding out each other over tankards of ale on the prospects of selling each other some horse, bull or pig which has passed its period of usefulness. In theory they take the view that beer is a great leveller and producer of generosity in the human spirit; in practice they remain as shrewd, sober and critical at closing-time as they were when they came in to drink. Mr. Sosserthwaite, considering himself vastly superior to his fellow farmers, sent his foreman along to the Bearpits on these occasions. He, poor chap, spent all night buying drinks and trying to sell a young bull for his master. The farmers, hugely enjoying any joke against Sosserthwaite, delighted in egging him on to buy more only for one of them to declare on the stroke of eleven: 'Tell un master that 'is bull be no use to my big cows. 'Twere like arsking an elephant to be mounted by a mouse.'

The book I should have written that summer was hopelessly delayed. If I imagined that, by leaving London and coming to the countryside, I could find more time to write, it was nothing but a delusion. There is far more to do in the country than in a town. In a village like Codiham, something is always going on. Probably, if one lived like a hermit, one could retain a sophisticated indifference to one's environment and such mundane enjoyments as Treasure Hunts, village cricket, Venetian Carnivals on the Dentical, Hoppers' Balls and the exhibitions of the Artists' Society. But there is really very little point in living in a village if you don't mix with all its people and share their enthusiasm.

Even now, up at my study window in the top of the Oast House, I am aware of a score of things to distract me from finishing the last few paragraphs of this book. One corner of the pond is a patch of liquid sun making of the silent waters a sheet of burnished metal, out of which a swan, with superb disdain, sails like an eternal question mark. High above this scene, arrogant in the tree-tops, a heron has alighted. It must have strayed from the heronry over at Henty, probably indulging in a hunting expedition along the Dentical. It is odd to recall that in the Middle Ages the heron was regarded as a choice dish and was itself hunted by falcons. A full-grown heron was worth as much as a goose in those days and was stuffed with bread-crumbs, thyme, parsley, sage and endives before being roasted. But the heron is off again and I turn instead to the last over of the last cricket match of the season. Up to the wicket lumbers Bob Peart, desperately trying to find that fatal spot at the pavilion end. I really ought to tear this sheet of paper from the type-writer and go to see the finish of the match.

But no, there will always be a tomorrow. That is the most comforting thought in the countryside, the feeling of permanence and continuity: 'there's allus bin "cucking" on the Green and so 'twill allus be.' And Bob Peart will still be trundling up to the wicket next season, just as the blue-bells will lay a carpet of misty brilliance under the plum trees next April. Perhaps tonight, when the sun dips behind the Downs, Sylvia and I will walk to Ghost's Wood to see Westhurst Abbey's ruin in print-moonlight, sniffing the night-scented campion flowers as we stroll along the snaky, spooky, leaf-silenced Witch's Path, oblivious of all else but the violet-stained shadows on the Abbey's pillars, the whirring wings of innumer-able gauzy moths dancing a ballet of snow-flakes in a moon-bathed coppice, the call of the corncrake and the long, low screech of the owl, imitating so eerily the shrieks of tortured customs officers of two hundred years ago. Then, on the way back, hugging the hop-gardens fence, like two mild-eyed, but certainly not melancholic Lotus-Eaters, we can seek out the dream-offerings of Morpheus in the soporific tang of the hops, lured back to home and sleep by the clock of Saint Mildred's sweetly tolling eleven clear, unhurried notes.

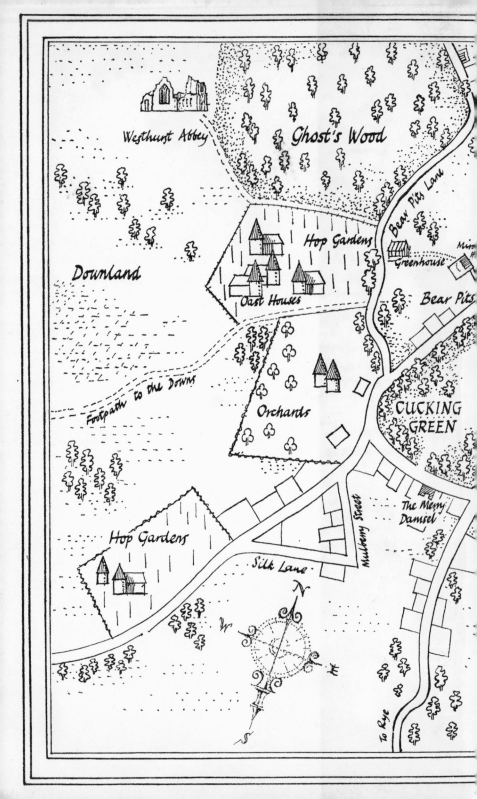